MATHEMATICAL STUDIES

A Series for Teachers and Students

EDITED BY

DAVID WHEELER

School of Education, University of Leicester

No. 4

SETS AND BOOLEAN ALGEBRA

D1600661

Sets and Boolean Algebra

By
MARCEL RUEFF
and
MAX JEGER

English version edited by A. G. Howson

New York
AMERICAN ELSEVIER PUBLISHING
COMPANY, Inc.
1970

American Edition Published by
American Elsevier Publishing Company, Inc.
52 Vanderbilt Avenue
New York, New York 10017

Standard Book Number 444–19751–6
Library of Congress Catalog Card Number 70–78910

PRINTED IN GREAT BRITAIN

FOREWORD

It is generally agreed that school mathematics syllabuses are in need of reform. The traditional syllabus is no longer an adequate preparation for mathematics as it is taught at a higher level; it indicates very little of the range of contemporary uses of mathematics; and it contains a high proportion of routine computation and manipulation at the expense of mathematical ideas which yield immediate enjoyment and satisfaction. A number of schools are now experimenting with new syllabuses which attempt to cure these faults.

Whether the experiments prove to be wholly successful or not, they are bringing a new element into the situation: an awareness that it is part of the job of the teacher of mathematics to inform himself about the relatively recent developments and changes in his subject. It is no longer possible to believe that developments in mathematics concern only the research mathematician and do not have any bearing on the mathematics taught in schools. This series of books is intended as a contribution to the reform of school mathematics by introducing to the reader some areas of mathematics which, broadly speaking, can be called modern, and which are beginning to have an influence on the content of school syllabuses.

The series does not put forward explicit advice about what mathematics to teach and how it should be taught. It is meant to be useful to those teachers and students in training who want to know more mathematics so that they can begin to take part in the existing experimental schemes, or modify them, or devise their own syllabus revisions, however modest. The books are elementary without being trivial: the mathematical knowledge they assume is roughly that of a traditional grammar school course, although substantial sections of all the books can be understood with less.

Now that the stability over a long period of school mathematics syllabuses seems to be coming to an end, it is to be hoped that a new orthodoxy does not succeed the old. The reform of mathematics teaching should be a continuing process, associated with a deepening study of the subject throughout every teacher's professional life. These books may help to start some teachers on that course of study.   D.W.

CONTENTS
page

1

ELEMENTARY OBSERVATIONS ABOUT SETS

1.1 THE CONCEPT OF SET; NOTATION; EQUIVALENCE OF SETS

Georg Cantor, creator of the theory of sets, gave the following definition of a set:

A set is a totality of certain well defined objects of our perception or thought—called the elements of the set.

In what follows we shall denote sets by capital letters.

Some examples of sets are:

A the set of all persons belonging to the Wilson family,
B the set of all right-angled triangles,
C the set of all telephone subscribers in the city of Bristol,
D the set of natural numbers from 1 to 9,
E the set of rational numbers between 0 and 1,
F the set of passenger trains running on the Southern Region,
G the set comprising the moon, the number 4, and Lecture Room 18,
H the set of all complex numbers satisfying the equation $x^3 + 1 = 0$,
J the set of symphony concerts given during the 1968 Edinburgh International Festival,
K the set of the colours red, blue, green, yellow, and black,
L the set of the pairs of numbers (x, y) for which $x^2 + y^2 = 4$.

A set can be described by listing its elements. In this case the elements are placed within braces. This is called *definition by enumeration*. For example,

$D = \{1, 2, 3, 4, 5, 6, 7, 8, 9\}$,
$G = \{\text{the moon, the number 4, Lecture Room 18}\}$.

It should be noted that the diameter of the moon, and the lights and doors of Lecture Room 18, do not form part of the set G; G has three elements only.

Another possible way of describing a set is by stating characteristic properties of its elements. In this case, *the set is defined by its characteristic features or attributes*. Examples of this kind of definition of a set are provided by the sets A and B above. This second method of describing a set may be expressed in the following way:

M is the set of all x for which $a(x)$ applies.

We shall write this as follows:

$$M = \{x \mid a(x)\}.$$

Thus, for example,

$$D = \{1, 2, 3, 4, 5, 6, 7, 8, 9\}$$
$$= \{x \mid x \text{ is a natural number}, x \leqslant 9\},$$
$$E = \{x \mid x \text{ is a rational number}, 0 < x < 1\}.$$

We shall introduce a special notation for some frequently occurring sets:

$N = \{1, 2, 3, \ldots\}$ the set of all natural numbers,

$N' = \{0, 1, 2, 3, \ldots\}$ the set of all non-negative integers,

$N_n = \{1, 2, 3, \ldots, n\}$ the set of all natural numbers from 1 to n,

Z　the set of integers,

Q　the set of rational numbers,

R　the set of real numbers,

C　the set of complex numbers.

Definition　Two sets A and B are said to be equal if they contain the same elements; for example,

$$\{1, 2, 4, 7\} = \{4, 7, 2, 1\}.$$

The order in which the elements are written is irrelevant.

If an element x forms part of a set M, we write $x \in M$ (say: x is an element of M, or x belongs to M). If y does not form part of the set M, we write $y \notin M$ (say: y is not an element of M, or y does not belong to M).

The set N_n may now also be defined as follows:

$$N_n = \{x \mid x \in N, x \leqslant n\}.$$

Thus, for example,

$$3 \in N_4, \qquad 7 \notin N_4.$$

Sometimes it may be convenient to associate the elements of one set A with the elements of a set B. One-to-one mappings are particularly important types of associations.

Definition Two sets A and B are said to be *equivalent* if there is a one-to-one relationship between the elements of A and the elements of B; we write $A \sim B$.

The relation $\sim$ defined on the sets A, B, C, . . . has the following properties:

1. $A \sim A$ property of reflexivity,
2. $(A \sim B) \Rightarrow (B \sim A)$ property of symmetry,
3. $[(A \sim B) \text{ and } (B \sim C)] \Rightarrow (A \sim C)$ property of transitivity.

Definition A relation which is reflexive, symmetrical and transitive is called an *equivalence relation*.

Problem 1 Which of the following are equivalence relations?

(a) The relation 'is perpendicular to' on the set of all straight lines in a plane;

(b) the relation 'is parallel to' on the set of all straight lines in a plane (two straight lines f and g are parallel if they have a common perpendicular);

(c) the relation 'is congruent to' on the set of all triangles;

(d) the relation 'is similar to' on the set of all triangles;

(e) the relation 'is less than or equal to' on the set Q;

(f) the relation 'is a factor of' on the set N;

(g) the relation 'is equal to' on the set N.

1.1.1 *Examples of equivalent sets*

1. The sets

$$S = \{1, 4, 7, 10, 13\} \text{ and } N_5 = \{1, 2, 3, 4, 5\}$$

are equivalent. The function

$$x \rightarrow y = f(x) = 3x - 2; \, x \in N_5$$

indicates the one-to-one relation between the elements of N and S.

Definition A set S which is equivalent to a set N_n is a *finite set*.

The number of elements in a finite set S is called the order of S. The number of elements in S is written $n(S)$. Obviously, we have the following equivalence of statements:

$$(S \sim N_5) \Leftrightarrow (n(S) = n(N_5) = 5).$$

2. As a second example, we mention the following interesting equivalence between two *infinite* sets:

$$E = \{x \,|\, x \in Q, 0 < x < 1\} \sim N.$$

In order to demonstrate this, we must produce a one-to-one mapping between the elements of E and those of N. Such a mapping can be obtained as follows.

An alternative description of E is

$$E = \left\{ x \,|\, x = \frac{p}{q}, \, p, q \in N, \, p < q \right\}.$$

We now arrange the elements of E first according to increasing denominators and then according to increasing numerators. Fractions which can be reduced can be omitted, since they have already been mentioned. Thus,

$$E = \left\{ \frac{1}{2}, \frac{1}{3}, \frac{2}{3}, \frac{1}{4}, \frac{2}{4}, \frac{3}{4}, \frac{1}{5}, \frac{2}{5}, \frac{3}{5}, \frac{4}{5}, \frac{1}{6}, \frac{2}{6}, \frac{3}{6}, \frac{4}{6}, \frac{5}{6}, \frac{1}{7}, \cdots \right\}.$$

This produces a well defined listing of the elements of E. The relation $\frac{1}{2} \rightarrow 1$, $\frac{1}{3} \rightarrow 2$, $\frac{2}{3} \rightarrow 3$, and so on, defines a one-to-one correspondence between the elements of E and those of N and demonstrates the equivalence of the two sets.

It may easily be shown that

$$M = \{x \mid x \in R, x^2+7x+12 = 0\} = \{-3, -4\}.$$

However, we note that

$$M' = \{x \mid x \in N, x^2+7x+12 = 0\}$$

is an empty set, because there is no natural number x which satisfies the equation $x^2+7x+12 = 0$.

Definition The set which contains no elements is called the *empty set;* it is denoted by the symbol $\emptyset$.

Problem 2 List the members of the following sets:

$$H_1 = \{x \mid x \in C, x^3+1 = 0\},$$
$$H_2 = \{x \mid x \in R, x^3+1 = 0\},$$
$$H_3 = \{x \mid x \in N, x^3+1 = 0\},$$
$$L_1 = \{(x, y) \mid x, y \in N, x^2+y^2 \leqslant 4\},$$
$$L_2 = \{(x, y) \mid x, y \in N', x^2+y^2 \leqslant 4\},$$
$$L_3 = \{(x, y) \mid x, y \in Z, x^2+y^2 \leqslant 4\}.$$

1.2 THE MOST IMPORTANT CONCEPTS IN THE THEORY OF SETS

1.2.1 *Subsets and partial orders*

Definition The set A is said to be a *subset* of B if all elements of A are also elements of the set B.

If A is a subset of B, we write $A \subset B$. The definition of a subset may be formally written as follows:

$$A \subset B \overset{\text{def}}{\Leftrightarrow} (x \in A \Rightarrow x \in B).$$

Thus, for example,

$$\{1, 2, 3, 5\} \subset N_6.$$

Note that

$$\{1\} \subset N_6 \quad \text{and} \quad 1 \in N_6.$$

The set consisting of the number 1 is a subset of N_6, but the number 1 is an element of N_6.

The statement $A \subset B$ does not exclude the possibility that simultaneously $B \subset A$. In view of the definition of the subset, there exist the following logical equivalences:

$$[(A \subset B) \wedge (B \subset A)] \Leftrightarrow (x \in A \Leftrightarrow x \in B) \Leftrightarrow (A = B).*$$

If $A \subset B$ and $A \neq B$, there exists an element q such that $q \in B$ and $q \notin A$. In this case, A is a *proper* subset of B; e.g., $\{1, 2, 3, 5\}$ is a *proper* subset of N_6, because $4 \in N_6$ but $4 \notin \{1, 2, 3, 5\}$.

The relation $A \subset B$ has a certain similarity with the relation $a \leqslant b$ defined on the set R. It has the following properties in common with the latter:

1. $A \subset A$ property of reflexivity,
2. $[(A \subset B) \wedge (B \subset A)] \Rightarrow (A = B)$ property of anti-symmetry,
3. $[(A \subset B) \wedge (B \subset C)] \Rightarrow (A \subset C)$ property of transitivity.

However, there is a fundamental difference between $\subset$ and the order relation $\leqslant$ on the set R: while at least one of the two relations $a \leqslant b$ or $b \leqslant a$ holds for every pair of numbers a, $b \in R$, the same is not true for sets. Thus, for example, if $A = \{1, 2, 3\}$ and $B = \{2, 3, 4\}$, then neither $A \subset B$ nor $B \subset A$. The relation $A \subset B$ determines only a *partial* ordering, while $a \leqslant b$ determines a simple (or total) ordering.

Definition   A reflexive, anti-symmetric and transitive relation is a *partial ordering*.

Problem 3   Which of the following relations are partial orderings:

(a) $x, y \in N$; relation $x \mid y$ (x is a factor of y);
(b) x, y are straight lines of a plane; relation $x \parallel y$;
(c) S is the set of the pupils in a form: $x, y \in S$; relation 'x is at least as old as y'?

$*\wedge$ is the logical connective equivalent to 'and'.

Definition   The set of all subsets of a set U is called the *power set* of U; it is denoted by $P(U)$.

$$P(U) \overset{\text{def}}{\Leftrightarrow} \{X \mid X \subset U\}.$$

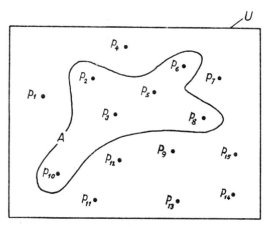

Fig. 1

Figure 1 shows the subset

$$A = \{p_2, p_3, p_5, p_6, p_8, p_{10}\}$$

of the finite point set

$$U = \{p_1, p_2, \ldots, p_{15}\}.$$

Note

$$A \subset U, \qquad A \in P(U);$$

that is, A is a subset of U, but A is an element of $P(U)$.

Since the empty set is contained in every set U, it is an element of the power set $P(U)$.

The power set for N_3 may be written in full:

$$P(N_3) = \{\varnothing, \{1\}, \{2\}, \{3\}, \{1, 2\}, \{1, 3\}, \{2, 3\}, \{1, 2, 3\}\}.$$

Problem 4   List in full the power set of

$$U = \{a, b, c, d\}.$$

The relation of set inclusion, $A \subset B$, gives a partial ordering on a set of sets

$$\Omega = \{A, B, C, \ldots\}.$$

When Ω is finite this may be illustrated by means of a graph. Each element of Ω is represented by a point in the plane of the drawing. If $A \subset B$, the image point of A is placed under the image point of B and the two points are connected by a line. For $\Omega = P(N_3)$, we obtain Figure 2a.

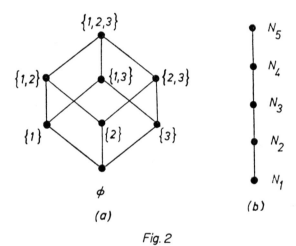

ϕ

(a)

(b)

Fig. 2

This is called the *Hasse diagram* of the given partial ordering on Ω. The Hasse diagram for the system of sets

$$\sum_5 = \{N_1, N_2, N_3, N_4, N_5\}$$

is shown in Figure 2b. This type of diagram is called a *chain*. Simple orderings are always represented by chains.

Problem 5 Let $F(n)$ be the set of all factors of the natural number n. The relation 'a is a factor of b' defines a partial ordering on $F(n)$. Draw the corresponding Hasse diagrams for $F(30)$ and $F(60)$ and compare them with Figure 2a.

1.2.2 *Set operations*

Definition The *union* of A and B consists of all elements which belong to at least one of the two sets A and B. It is denoted by $A \cup B$.

In formal notation the definition of the union is:

$$A \cup B \overset{\text{def}}{\Leftrightarrow} \{x \,|\, (x \in A) \vee (x \in B)\}.*$$

For example,

$$\{1, 3, 4\} \cup \{1, 2, 3, 5, 7\} = \{1, 2, 3, 4, 5, 7\}.$$

Definition The *intersection* of A and B consists of all elements which belong to both A and B. It is denoted by $A \cap B$.

Formally,

$$A \cap B \overset{\text{def}}{\Leftrightarrow} \{x \,|\, (x \in A) \wedge (x \in B)\}.$$

For example,

(a) $\{1, 3, 4\} \cap \{1, 2, 3, 5, 7\} = \{1, 3\}.$
(b) If $A = \{x \,|\, x \in N, x > 10\}$ and
$B = \{x \,|\, x \in R, x^2 - 7x + 12 = 0\},$

then $A \cap B = \varnothing$; A and B have no common elements. In this case, A and B are called *disjoint* sets.

Definition The Cartesian product of A and B, written $A \times B$, is the set of all pairs (x, y) with $x \in A$ and $y \in B$.

Formally,

$$A \times B \overset{\text{def}}{\Leftrightarrow} \{(x, y) \,|\, (x \in A) \wedge (y \in B)\}.$$

For example,

(a) $N_2 \times N_3 = \{(1, 1), (1, 2), (1, 3), (2, 1), (2, 2), (2, 3)\}.$
(b) If A is the set of throws of a coin, i.e., $A = \{\text{head, tail}\}$, then:

$A \times A = \{(\text{head, head}), (\text{head, tail}), (\text{tail, head}), (\text{tail, tail})\},$

the set of all possible throws of two coins.

---

* $\vee$ is the logical connective denoting 'and/or', also called the 'inclusive or'.

In practice, one frequently encounters situations in which all the sets under consideration are subsets of a readily distinguishable set U. The set U is then called the *universal set* for this problem.

If a universal set U is present, every set $A \subset U$ defines in a natural manner, a second set, namely the set A', comprising those elements of U which do not belong to A.

Definition   The set

$$A' = \{x \,|\, (x \in U) \wedge (x \notin A)\}$$

is the *complement* of A in U.

This definition leads directly to:

$$U' = \varnothing, \qquad \varnothing' = U,$$
$$A \cup A' = U, \quad A \cap A' = \varnothing \quad \text{for all } A \subset U.$$

1.2.3   *Finite sets. The Venn diagram*

Finite sets, or relations between such sets, are normally represented by means of equivalent point sets. A closed curve is drawn to enclose the point representing the elements of set A.* Generally, the designations of the elements and sets are transferred to the drawing. An example is shown in Figure 3.

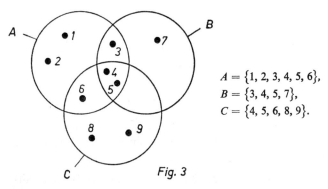

$A = \{1, 2, 3, 4, 5, 6\},$
$B = \{3, 4, 5, 7\},$
$C = \{4, 5, 6, 8, 9\}.$

Fig. 3

---

*It is often convenient to draw the closed curves as circles. However, any irregular loop will suffice and indeed we shall meet cases, see for example Figure 39, where circles cannot be used.

This representation is called a *Venn diagram* of the corresponding set configuration. The universal set U is usually indicated by a rectangle (see, for example, Figure 1).

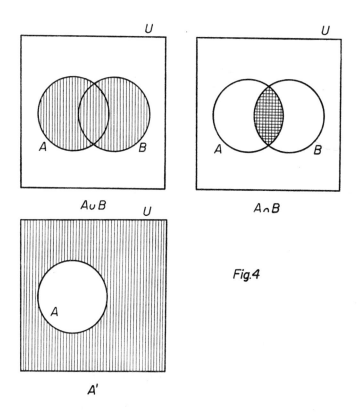

$A \cup B$

$A \cap B$

A'

Fig.4

In many cases, it is unnecessary to mark the points corresponding to the individual set elements, and the regions within the closed lines may be regarded as representing the associated sets. In this somewhat more liberal application of the Venn diagram, union, intersection and forming the complement may be represented as shown in Figure 4.

When calculating with cardinal numbers, the following fundamental relation holds:

$$n(A \cup B) + n(A \cap B) = n(A) + n(B), \tag{1}$$

as shown in Figure 5. If $A \cap B = \emptyset$, (1) simplifies, since $n(\emptyset) = 0$, to

$$n(A \cup B) = n(A) + n(B). \tag{2}$$

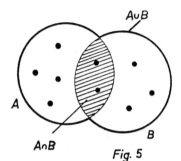

Fig. 5

Problem 6 Show that:

(a) $n(A \times B) = n(A) \cdot n(B)$,

(b) $\underbrace{n(A \times A \times A \times \ldots \times A)}_{s \text{ factors}} = [n(A)]^s$.

If A is a subset of U, then for every $x \in U$ either

$$x \in A \quad \text{or} \quad x \notin A.$$

If there are two subsets A, B of U, every $x \in U$ will therefore be in exactly one of the four sets

$$M_1 = A \cap B, \; M_2 = A \cap B', \; M_3 = A' \cap B, \; M_4 = A' \cap B'.$$

The sets M_1, M_2, M_3, M_4, intersect pair-wise in the empty set. Figure 6 shows the Venn diagram illustrating this general situation.

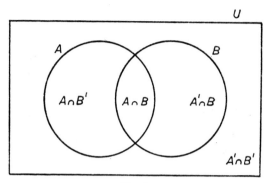

Fig. 6

Definition The sets K_1, K_2, . . . , K_n form a *partition* of the set U if:

(a) $K_1 \cup K_2 \cup \ldots \cup K_n = U$,

(b) $K_i \cap K_j = \emptyset$ for all pairs $i \neq j$,

(c) $K_j \neq \emptyset$ for $j = 1, 2, \ldots, n$.

If none of the above-mentioned sets M_1, M_2, M_3, M_4 is empty, then they form a partition of U. This is called the partition of U resulting from the two subsets A and B.

Similarly, starting with the three elements A, B, and C of $P(U)$, one can decompose U into eight subsets such that every $x \in U$ is in exactly one of these subsets. These eight subsets are:

$$M_1 = (A \cap B) \cap C, \qquad M_5 = (A' \cap B') \cap C,$$
$$M_2 = (A' \cap B) \cap C, \qquad M_6 = (A' \cap B) \cap C',$$
$$M_3 = (A \cap B') \cap C, \qquad M_7 = (A \cap B') \cap C',$$
$$M_4 = (A \cap B) \cap C', \qquad M_8 = (A' \cap B') \cap C'.$$

The subsets are represented in the Venn diagram in Figure 7. Naturally, some of these sets may be empty. If this is not the case, then there is a partition of U resulting from its three subsets A, B and C.

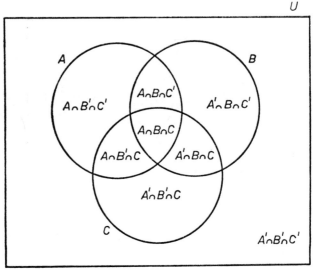

Fig. 7

If X and Y are two elements of $P(U)$, the following five statements are obviously equivalent:

$$X \subset Y;\ X \cup Y = Y;\ X \cap Y = X;\ X' \cup Y = U;\ X \cap Y' = \emptyset.$$

This can be seen directly from Figure 8.

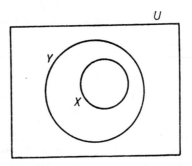

Fig. 8

1.2.4 *The basic laws of the algebra of finite sets*

In the definitions of union and intersection (see section 1.2.2), the sets A and B occur symmetrically, i.e.,

1a. $A \cup B = B \cup A$,   1b. $A \cap B = B \cap A$.

Union and intersection are *commutative*.

Either of the operations is *distributive* over the other; i.e.,

2a. $A \cup (B \cap C) =$ 2b. $A \cap (B \cup C) =$
$\quad (A \cup B) \cap (A \cup C)$, $\quad (A \cap B) \cup (A \cap C)$.

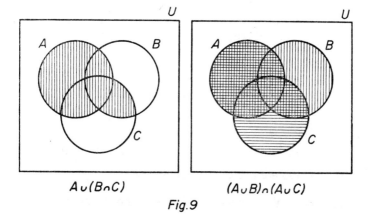

$A \cup (B \cap C)$ $(A \cup B) \cap (A \cup C)$

Fig. 9

The representation of both sides of equation 2a by Venn diagrams leads to the same region in both cases; we may therefore conclude that the equation is correct (Figure 9).

The laws 2a and 2b show a marked difference from those of elementary algebra; there one has only the distributive law of multiplication over addition.

Quite obviously, the following two laws also apply:

3a. $A \cup \emptyset = \emptyset \cup A = A$,   3b. $A \cap U = U \cap A = A$.

Thus, the empty set $\emptyset$ is the identity or unit element for the union operation, whilst this role is played for the intersection operation by the universal set U.

For each element A there is an element A' satisfying

4a. $A \cup A' = U$ and   4b. $A \cap A' = \emptyset$.

It may be seen immediately that the operations of union and intersection are *associative*; i.e.,

5a. $A \cup (B \cup C) =$ 5b. $A \cap (B \cap C) =$
        $(A \cup B) \cup C,$ $(A \cap B) \cap C.$

We shall now mention further laws which can be easily verified by means of Venn diagrams:

6a. $A \cup A = A,$ 6b. $A \cap A = A.$

These are the two *idempotent laws*. In the algebra of sets a summand may be repeated as many times as desired, and there are no powers.

7a. $A \cup (A \cap B) = A,$ 7b. $A \cap (A \cup B) = A.$

Formulae 7a and 7b are called *absorption laws*.

8a. $A \cup U = U,$ 8b. $A \cap \emptyset = \emptyset.$
9a. $\emptyset' = U,$ 9b. $U' = \emptyset.$
10a. $(A \cup B)' = A' \cap B',$ 10b. $(A \cap B)' = A' \cup B'.$

10a and 10b are known as *de Morgan's laws*.

Problem 7   Verify laws 6 to 10 by means of Venn diagrams.

Problem 8   Compare laws 1 to 10 with the laws governing numerical calculations. Which of the laws of the algebra of sets have an analogue, if the operations $\cup$ and $\cap$ are taken to correspond to $+$ and $\times$ respectively?

Some of the laws 1 to 10 occur also in the definition of a field.* However, there are a substantial number of laws for which no analogues exist in this particular structure.

Laws 1 to 10 form a possible *logical basis for the algebra of sets;* the whole algebra of sets can be obtained from them by pure deduction. This basis can be substantially refined and we

*See, for example, [13].

shall show in Section 2.2 that laws 1 to 4 are sufficient; laws 5 to 10 can be derived from them.

In setting up the basic laws of the algebra of sets, we have tried to present the laws in pairs. This principle can be observed throughout. We always have to interchange the signs $\cup$ and $\cap$, and the elements U and $\emptyset$, in one of the laws in order to obtain its partner. We see that:

If the operations $\cup$ and $\cap$, and the elements U and $\emptyset$, are interchanged, then the totality of the 20 basic laws is mapped onto itself; these interchanges effect an automorphism of the basic laws.

The laws thus possess the remarkable property of *duality*.*

Note: Laws 1 to 10 hold in every power set (see p. 13). The proof of this is a problem in elementary logic.

1.3 APPLICATIONS

1.3.1 *Set operations and Venn diagrams*

Example The population of a town was tested for blood groups; every person was checked for the presence of A and B antigens and of the Rhesus factor.

In this example, there are four precisely defined sets:

$U = \{$tested persons$\}$,

$A = \{$carriers of antigen A$\}$,

$B = \{$carriers of antigen B$\}$,

$R = \{$persons with Rhesus factor, i.e. Rh$+$ persons$\}$.

First, the sets A and B cause the splitting up of the universal set U into four classes, each of which corresponds to one of the ordinary blood groups:

		Blood group
$A \cap B$	$= \{$carrier of antigen A and antigen B$\}$	**AB**
$A \cap B'$	$= \{$persons having only the antigen A$\}$	**A**
$A' \cap B$	$= \{$persons having only the antigen B$\}$	**B**
$A' \cap B'$	$= \{$persons having neither antigen A nor B$\}$	**O**

*The implications of this property will be seen in later sections.

The three sets A, B and R lead to a division of U into more finely differentiated blood groups:

$A \cap B \cap R$ = {persons with blood group AB with Rh+},
$A' \cap B' \cap R$ = {persons with blood group O with Rh+},
$A \cap B' \cap R$ = {persons with blood group A with Rh+},
$A' \cap B \cap R$ = {persons with blood group B with Rh+},
$A \cap B \cap R'$ = {persons with blood group AB with Rh−},
$A' \cap B' \cap R'$ = {persons with blood group O with Rh−},
$A \cap B' \cap R'$ = {persons with blood group A with Rh−},
$A' \cap B \cap R'$ = {persons with blood group B with Rh−}.

It should be mentioned in passing that, whenever possible, the donor and receiver in blood transfusions should always belong to the same group. The following diagram shows the different possibilities:

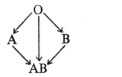

Problem 9 On the basis of numerous investigations in Switzerland the following relative frequencies were found for the presence of antigens A and B:

Carriers of antigen A   48%
Carriers of antigen B   10%
Carriers of both antigens A and B   3%

What is the percentage distribution of the four blood groups A, B, AB and O?

The Venn diagram of Figure 10 gives an immediate answer, because we have sufficient information about the four subsets. The universal set has, of course, the frequency 100%.

Blood group	Blood group
O 45%	B 7%
A 45%	AB 3%

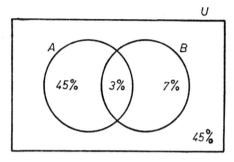

Fig. 10

Problem 10 In a statistical investigation of 1003 households, it was found that 63 households had neither a radio nor a television set. 794 families had a radio and 187 a television. How many of the families sampled had both?

Problem 11 A statistical investigation of the foreign languages studied by 100 university students gave the following results:

German	26
French	48
French and Spanish	8
German but not Spanish	23
Only German	18
German and French	8
No foreign language	24

(a) How many take Spanish?

(b) How many take German and Spanish, but not French?

(c) How many take German, as well as Spanish or French or both?

For the solution, we introduce the following sets:

$U = \{$students in the sample$\}$, the universal set,

$F = \{$students taking French$\}$,

$G = \{$students taking German$\}$,

$S = \{$students taking Spanish$\}$.

The sets F, G, S again produce a division of U into eight subsets. It is possible to determine the orders of these eight subsets, since we are given eight items of information. So as to answer the three questions, we must determine the number of elements in the three sets S, A and B.

$$A = G \cap S \cap F', \qquad B = G \cap (S \cup F),$$
$$n(S) = 18,$$
$$n(A) = 0,$$
$$n(B) = 8.$$

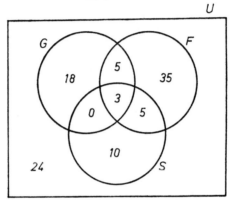

Fig. 11

Problem 12 Three players, Alfred, Bruno and Caesar, each draw a card from a complete pack. Such a triple draw is called a trial. The cards drawn are always returned to the pack before a further trial. Altogether the trial is repeated 50 times. It is then found that:

Alfred has drawn a red card in 35 trials,

Bruno has drawn a red card in 25 trials,

Caesar has drawn a red card in 28 trials,

Alfred and Bruno have both drawn red cards in 15 trials,

Bruno and Caesar have both drawn red cards in 13 trials.

What can be said about the number of trials in which all three players drew red cards?*

*This example is taken from: Félix L.: *Exposé moderne de mathématiques élémentaires*, Paris 1959.

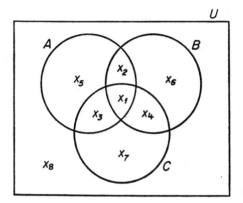

Fig. 12

The following sets are introduced in order to solve the problem:

U = {completed trials}, the universal set,
A = {trials in which Alfred draws a red card},
B = {trials in which Bruno draws a red card},
C = {trials in which Caesar draws a red card}.

The following data are given:

$$n(U) = 50, n(A) = 35, n(B) = 25, n(C) = 28,$$
$$n(A \cap B) = 15, n(B \cap C) = 13.$$

As before, the sets A, B and C produce a division of U into eight classes. Since we have only six items of information, the cardinal numbers of the eight classes will depend on two parameters. After introducing the cardinal numbers x_i, $i = 1, \ldots, 8$, corresponding to the classes in the Venn diagram in Figure 12, we find:

$$
\begin{align}
n(A) &= x_1 + x_2 + x_3 + x_5 = 35, \tag{1}\\
n(B) &= x_1 + x_2 + x_4 + x_6 = 25, \tag{2}\\
n(C) &= x_1 + x_3 + x_4 + x_7 = 28, \tag{3}\\
n(A \cap B) &= x_1 + x_2 = 15, \tag{4}\\
n(B \cap C) &= x_1 + x_4 = 13, \tag{5}\\
n(U) &= \sum_{i=1}^{8} x_i = 50. \tag{6}
\end{align}
$$

We introduce the two parameters $\xi = x_1$ and $\eta = x_8$. It follows directly that:

$$
\begin{array}{ll}
x_2 = 15 - \xi & \text{[from (4)]}, \\
x_4 = 13 - \xi & \text{[from (5)]}, \\
x_6 = 25 - (x_1 + x_2 + x_4) = \xi - 3 & \text{[from (2)]}.
\end{array}
$$

By substituting these values into equations (1), (3) and (6), we obtain:

$$
\begin{array}{ll}
x_3 + x_5 & = 20, \\
x_3 + x_7 & = 15, \\
x_3 + x_5 + x_7 & = 25 - \eta.
\end{array}
$$

From these, it is possible to express x_3, x_5 and x_7 in terms of the parameter η. Finally we can express x_i, $i = 2, \ldots, 7$, in terms of ξ and η:

$$
\begin{array}{ll}
x_2 = 15 - \xi, & x_5 = 10 - \eta, \\
x_3 = 10 + \eta, & x_6 = \xi - 3, \\
x_4 = 13 - \xi, & x_7 = 5 - \eta.
\end{array}
$$

Since the order of a set is a non-negative number, the parameters must satisfy the following inequalities:

$$
\begin{array}{l}
3 \leqslant \xi \leqslant 13, \\
0 \leqslant \eta \leqslant 5.
\end{array}
$$

It should be remembered that ξ is the number of trials in which all three players drew red cards, η the number of trials in which all three players drew black cards. We shall return to this example in Section 4.1 in connection with relative frequency.

Problem 13 The set

$$M = \{x \mid x \text{ natural number}, x \leqslant 50\}$$

contains the following subsets:

$A = \{x \mid x \in M, \text{ decimal representation of } x \text{ contains at least one digit 3}\}$,

$B = \{x \mid x \in M, x \text{ is divisible by } 8\}$,

$C = \{x \mid x \in M, \text{ decimal representation of } x \text{ contains only even digits}\}$.

(a) List the elements of the sets A, B and C and draw the corresponding Venn diagram. Mark each region with the order of the corresponding subset.

(b) Find a set $X \subset M$ which contains at least three elements and which satisfies

$$X \cap A = \emptyset, \ X \cap B = \emptyset, \ X \cap C = \emptyset.$$

(c) Describe the set C' without listing its elements.

(d) What is the order of the set D which comprises those elements that belong to exactly two of the three subsets A, B and C?

It is found that:

$A = \{3, 13, 23, 30, 31, 32, 33, 34, 35, 36, 37, 38, 39, 43\}$,
$B = \{8, 16, 24, 32, 40, 48\}$,
$C = \{2, 4, 6, 8, 20, 22, 24, 26, 28, 40, 42, 44, 46, 48\}$,

and knowing this we can draw the Venn diagram shown in Figure 13.

It should be noted that X must be a subset of

$$A' \cap B' \cap C' = (A \cup B \cup C)'$$

(see Section 2.2, Theorem 11).

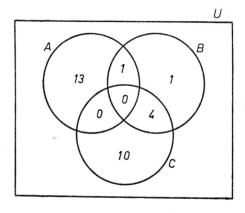

Fig. 13

The set C' can be written:

$C' = \{x \mid x \in M,\ x$ when expressed in decimal notation contains at least one odd digit$\}$.

The set D may be defined as

$$D = (A \cap B \cap C') \cup (A \cap B' \cap C) \cup (A' \cap B \cap C),$$

and from the Venn diagram we can see that the order of this set is

$$1 + 0 + 4 = 5.$$

Problem 14 Three players each throw a die 50 times. The dice are always thrown simultaneously. Such a triple throw is called a trial.

In 28 trials player I throws an odd number.

In 25 trials player II throws an even number.

In 27 trials player III throws an even number.

In 8 trials players I and III throw an odd and player II an even number.

In 7 trials players II and III throw an even and player I an odd number.

In 4 trials all three players throw odd numbers.

In 11 trials players II and III throw an odd number.

We introduce the following sets:

$A = \{$trials in which player I throws an even number$\}$,

$B = \{$trials in which player II throws an even number$\}$,

$C = \{$trials in which player III throws an even number$\}$.

(a) Illustrate the above data in a Venn diagram.

(b) Find the order of the sets R, S and T when

$R = \{$trials in which exactly one player throws an odd number$\}$,

$S = \{$trials in which at least one player throws an odd number$\}$,

$T = \{$trials in which the sum of the throws is an even number$\}$.

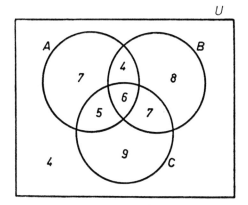

Fig.14

The Venn diagram in Figure 14 can be constructed from the given data.

The sets R and S can be expressed as follows:

$$R = (A' \cap B \cap C) \cup (A \cap B' \cap C) \cup (A \cap B \cap C'),$$
$$S = A' \cup B' \cup C' = (A \cap B \cap C)'.$$

From the Venn diagram we see that

$$n(R) = 16,$$
$$n(S) = 44.$$

The sum of the throws will be an even number if either all three players throw an even number, or if one player throws an even number and the other two odd numbers. This gives the following definition of the set T:

$$T = (A \cap B' \cap C') \cup (A' \cap B \cap C') \cup (A' \cap B' \cap C) \cup (A \cap B \cap C),$$

and the order of T, $n(T)$, is 30.

1.3.2   Sets of factors

In this section a, b, $c \in N$. We have already introduced the concept of a set of factors in Problem 5:

$$F(a) = \{x \mid x \in N, x \text{ is a factor of } a\}.$$

For example,

$$F(7) \;= \{1, 7\},$$
$$F(10) = \{1, 2, 5, 10\},$$
$$F(12) = \{1, 2, 3, 4, 6, 12\}.$$

Let $a*b$ denote the greatest common divisor (GCD) of a and b.

Problem 15 Prove the following rules for sets of factors:

I $F(a) \cap F(b) = F(a*b)$,

II. $F(a) \cap F(ab) = F(a)$,

III. $F(a) \cap F(a+c) = F(a) \cap F(c)$,

IV. $F(a) \cap F(ab+c) = F(a) \cap F(c)$,

V. $F(a) = F(b) \Leftrightarrow a = b$.

Using rules I to V of Problem 15, we can represent the *Euclidean algorithm* for producing $a*b$ in terms of sets of factors. For example,

$$
\begin{aligned}
F(1715*945) &= F(1715) \cap F(945) \\
&= F(1.945+770) \cap F(945) = F(945) \cap F(770) \\
&= F(1.770+175) \cap F(770) = F(770) \cap F(175) \\
&= F(4.175+70) \cap F(175) = F(175) \cap F(70) \\
&= F(2.70+35) \cap F(70) = F(70) \cap F(35) \\
&= F(2.35) \cap F(35) = F(35).
\end{aligned}
$$

Thus

$$F(1715*945) = F(35) \Leftrightarrow 1715*945 = 35.$$

Problem 16 Using the above method, find:

(a) $3816*5184$,

(b) $360*984*648$.

Note that $a*b*c = (a*b)*c$.

1.3.3   *The set system* $\sum = \{N_0, N_1, N_2, \ldots\}$

For reasons of consistency, in this section we shall denote the empty set, $\varnothing$, by N_0.

It is clear that in Σ,

$$N_j \cup N_k = N_p \text{ where } p = \max (j, k),$$
$$N_j \cap N_k = N_q \text{ where } q = \min (j, k).$$

The set Σ is closed under the operations of union and inter-section.

Set inclusion produces a simple ordering in Σ, because

$$N_j \subset N_k \Leftrightarrow j \leqslant k.$$

Problem 17 Draw the Hasse diagram (see p. 14) for the set Σ.

The finite set

$$\Sigma_n = \{N_0, N_1, N_2, \ldots, N_n\}$$

is a subset of the power set $P(N_n)$. If a finite number of elements of Σ are combined, then one always obtains a set in which the fundamental laws of Section 1.2.4 apply.

The associative law for union leads to:

$$N_i \cup \underbrace{(N_j \cup N_k)}_{N_p} = \underbrace{(N_i \cup N_j)}_{N_q} \cup N_k = N_s,$$

where

$$p = \max(j, k),\ q = \max(i, j),\ s = \max(i, p) = \max(q, k).$$

This leads directly to the relation

$$\max(i, \max(j, k)) = \max(\max(i, j), k)$$

for $i, j, k \in N' = N \cup \{0\}$.

In the same way we obtain from the associative law for intersection:

$$\min(i, \min(j, k)) = \min(\min(i, j), k)$$

for $i, j, k \in N'$.

Problem 18 Using the distributive or absorption laws in Σ, show that the following relations are satisfied by $i, j,\ k \in N'$.

(a) $\max(i, \min(j, k)) = \min(\max(i, j), \max(i, k))$,

(b) $\min(i, \max(j, k)) = \max(\min(i, j), \min(i, k))$,

(c) $\max(i, \min(i, j)) = i;\ \min(i, \max(i, j)) = i$.

Problem 19 Verify the laws found for N' by means of concrete numerical examples.

Our investigations were based on the set Σ with the operations $\cup$ and $\cap$. We shall call this system $[\Sigma, \cup, \cap]$. From this point, we arrived at the system $[N', \max, \min]$.

$n(N_j) = j$ defines a mapping of the system $[\Sigma, \cup, \cap]$ onto the system $[N', \max, \min]$ in which the following correspondences are observed:

$[\Sigma, \cup, \cap]$	$[N', \max, \min]$
N_j	j
$N_j \subset N_k$	$j \leqslant k$
$N_j \cup N_k$	$\max(j, k)$
$N_j \cap N_k$	$\min(j, k)$

The two systems $[\Sigma, \cup, \cap]$ and $[N', \max, \min]$ have the same algebraic structures; they are said to be *isomorphic algebraic systems*.

1.3.4 *The relation between set inclusion in $P(U)$, union and intersection*

Set inclusion, $A \subset B$, is a relation on $P(U)$ whose properties can be deduced completely from the laws 1 to 10 (Section 1.2.4) which we know hold in $P(U)$. In this section we shall show how we can establish these facts by means of calculations with sets.

We begin with the equivalence

$$A \subset B \Leftrightarrow A \cap B = A.$$

Next we show that

$$A \cap B = A \Leftrightarrow A \cup B = B. \qquad \text{I}$$

Proof

(a) It follows from the assumption $A \cap B = A$, that

$$B = B \cup (B \cap A) = B \cup (A \cap B) = B \cup A = A \cup B.$$

(b) Conversely, given $A \cup B = B$, then

$$A = A \cap (A \cup B) = A \cap B.$$

Now we prove that

$$A \cap B = A \Leftrightarrow A \cap B' = \emptyset. \qquad \text{II}$$

Proof

(a) Given $A \cap B = A$, then

$$A \cap B' = (A \cap B) \cap B' = A \cap (B \cap B') = \emptyset.$$

(b) Conversely, given $A \cap B' = \emptyset$, then

$$A = A \cap U = A \cap (B \cup B') = (A \cap B) \cup (A \cap B')$$
$$= (A \cap B) \cup \emptyset = A \cap B.$$

We now show that the relation is reflexive, i.e.

$$A \subset A. \qquad\qquad \text{III}$$

Proof This follows from

$$A \cap A = A.$$

Also, the relation is anti-symmetric; i.e.,

$$(A \subset B) \wedge (B \subset A) \Rightarrow A = B. \qquad \text{IV}$$

Proof Making use of the equivalences obtained above, we can rewrite the assumptions as $A \cap B = A$ and $B \cap A = B$. It follows, therefore, that $A = B$.

Finally we show that the relation is transitive; i.e.,

$$(A \subset B) \wedge (B \subset C) \Rightarrow A \subset C. \qquad \text{V}$$

We can again rewrite this in the form

$$(A \cap B = A) \wedge (B \cap C = B) \Rightarrow A \cap C = A.$$

Proof

$$A \cap C = (A \cap B) \cap C = A \cap (B \cap C) = A \cap B = A.$$

Problem 20 Verify that

$$A \subset B \Leftrightarrow B' \subset A'. \qquad\qquad \text{VI}$$

1.4 ILLUSTRATION OF ELEMENTARY COMBINATORIAL PROBLEMS BY MEANS OF SETS

The concepts of *permutations*, *combinations* and *statistical samples* present students with several problems, which are generally understood only after a long series of examples. The student is faced with the task of extracting the common core and with it the associated concept from concrete exercises. Experience has shown that the use of sets and of mappings between sets greatly facilitates understanding during the introduction of these topics. In this section we shall discuss models of sets which are suitable for this purpose.

We shall consider two finite sets S and K with the orders s and k.

Definition If each element $x \in S$ corresponds to exactly one element $f(x) \in K$, the correspondence is called a *mapping*. The element $y \in K$, corresponding to the element $x \in S$, is called the *image* of x under the map f.

This relationship may also be expressed as follows:

$$x \overset{f}{\to} y.$$

If the set of the images is denoted by $f(S)$, i.e.,

$$f(S) = \{f(x) \mid x \in S\},$$

it is, of course, always true that

$$f(S) \subset K.$$

Two cases can be distinguished with regard to $f(S)$:

(a) $f(S)$ is a proper subset of K, in which case we call f a mapping of the set S *into* the set K.

(b) $f(S) = K$, i.e., all elements of K occur as images of elements of S. In this case we say that f maps the set S *onto* the set K.

Two examples with sets of numbers will clarify this distinction. The correspondences between the elements of S and the elements of K are indicated by arrows.

Example 1 This is a mapping of the set S into the set K. It can be easily described, since we have

$$y = x + 5.$$

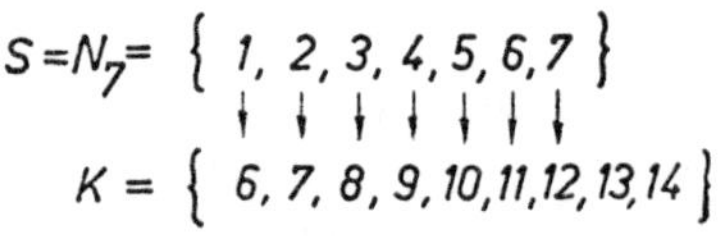

$$S = N_7 = \left\{ 1, 2, 3, 4, 5, 6, 7 \right\}$$
$$\downarrow \downarrow \downarrow \downarrow \downarrow \downarrow \downarrow$$
$$K = \left\{ 6, 7, 8, 9, 10, 11, 12, 13, 14 \right\}$$

Fig. 15

Example 2   The following sets are given:

$$S = \{1, 2, 3, 4, 5, 6, 7, 8\},$$
$$K = \{0, 1, 2\}.$$

We map each element of S onto that element of K to which it is congruent modulo 3 (i.e. x is mapped onto y if x leaves the remainder y when divided by 3). The mapping so defined is indicated in Figure 16 by means of arrows.

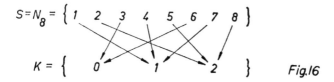

Fig.16

Every element of K is the image of some element of S, and we have a mapping of S onto K.

Apart from the distinction between a mapping of S into K and a mapping of S onto K, these examples also demonstrate another essential difference. In Example 1, each element of K which occurs as an image is the image of exactly one element of S, whilst in Example 2, an element of K is the image of more than one element of S. The mapping of Example 1 is *single-valued* in both directions.

Definition   A mapping of S onto K, in which every element of K is the image of exactly one element of S, is called a *one-to-one correspondence*.

The basic combinatorial problems can now be described clearly by means of mappings of S into or onto K.

Problem 21   The sets S and K have the same orders. How many one-to-one correspondences between the sets are there? We represent the elements of the sets S and K by points and denote the elements of S by x_i, $i = 1, \ldots, s$. Since there is a one-to-one mapping onto K, exactly one arrow will end at each element of K (Figure 17). For $f(x_1)$, there are s possibilities. If $f(x_1)$ is fixed, there are $s-1$ possibilities for $f(x_2)$. If $f(x_1)$

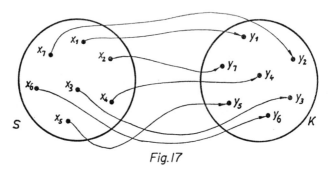

Fig. 17

and $f(x_2)$ are given, there still remain $s-2$ free positions in K for $f(x_3)$, etc. From this one obtains the following formula for the number of possible one-to-one mappings of S onto K:

$$P_s = s(s-1)(s-2) \ldots 2.1 = s!.$$

If the sets S and K are identified, every mapping of S onto K yields a one-to-one mapping of the set S onto itself. This is equivalent to an interchange of the elements of S amongst themselves. Hence, P_s is the number of permutations of s elements.

Example In how many ways can s persons sit on s chairs?

This relates to the number of one-to-one correspondences between the set S of persons and the set K of chairs.

Problem 22 How many mappings of a set S are there (a) *into*, and (b) *onto*, a set K?

If $k > s$, then there are only mappings *into* K. On the other hand, if $k \leqslant s$, then mappings onto K may also occur.

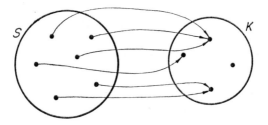

Fig. 18

Figure 18 shows a mapping into K for $k < s$, whilst Figure 19 shows a mapping onto K for $k < s$. The method of counting the possible mappings does not depend on the relative magnitudes of k and s.

Every element of K may be the image of any element of S. The set of possible mappings is therefore equivalent to the set

$$\underbrace{K \times K \times K \times \ldots \times K}_{s \text{ factors}}$$

Thus the number of mappings is

$$n(K \times K \times K \times \ldots \times K) = [n(K)]^s = k^s.$$

Each of these mappings characterizes an *s-sample*, with repetitions, of a k-set.

Problem 23 How many possible outcomes are there of a football pool with 12 games?

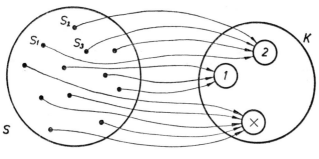

Fig.19

Figure 19 shows one possible outcome; this situation corresponds to a mapping of the set S of games onto the set K of possible results: 1 home win, 2 away win, $\times$ draw. Thus there are 3^{12} possible ways of filling in a pools coupon to forecast the results of 12 games.

Problem 24 Find the number of one-to-one mappings of a set S into or onto a set K, respectively.

Since a one-to-one relationship is required, the condition $k \geqslant s$ must be satisfied. For $k = s$, the mappings will be onto K, for $k > s$ mappings into K. We set

$$S = \{x_1, x_2, x_3, \ldots, x_s\},$$

and have k possibilities for $f(x_1)$. If $f(x_1)$ is given, $k-1$ possibilities remain for $f(x_2)$, because one element of K is already occupied by $f(x_1)$ and the mapping must be one-to-one.

If $f(x_1)$ and $f(x_2)$ are given, $k-2$ possibilities remain for $f(x_3)$, etc.; if the images of x_i up to $i = s-1$ are given, there remain finally $k-s+1$ possibilities for choosing $f(x_s)$. Hence, we find that the number of one-to-one mappings, $P(k, s)$, is

$$k(k-1)(k-2)\ldots(k-s+1) = \begin{cases} \dfrac{k!}{(k-s)!} & \text{for } k > s, \\ k! & \text{for } k = s. \end{cases}$$

We note that $P(k, k) = k!$.

In this way, we have counted the number of samples without repetitions of s elements of a set of order k. Such a sample is called an s-permutation of k elements. For $k = s$, this exercise is the same as that already solved in Problem 21, which gave the number of permutations of k elements.

Problem 25 How many two-digit numbers can be formed using the nine symbols 1 to 9 (repetitions such as 22 are not allowed)?

In this example, S is the set of the two places, U (units) and T (tens). These must be mapped onto different elements of the set $K = \{1, 2, 3, \ldots, 9\}$. We find that the number of such one-to-one mappings of S into K (see Figure 20) is $9!/7!$, i.e. 72.

Problem 26 Find the number of mappings of S onto K, given the frequency with which each element of K occurs as image.

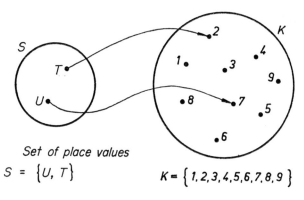

Set of place values

$$S = \{U, T\} \qquad K = \{1, 2, 3, 4, 5, 6, 7, 8, 9\}$$

Fig. 20

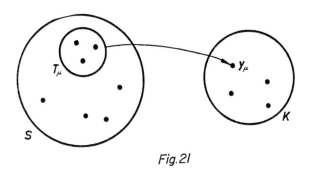

Fig. 21

Since we consider mappings of S onto K, we must have $s \geq k$. Denote the sets S and K as follows:

$$S = \{x_1, x_2, x_3, \ldots, x_s\},$$
$$K = \{y_1, y_2, y_3, \ldots, y_k\},$$

and let α_μ denote the number of times the element y_μ occurs as image. It is a consequence of the uniqueness of the definition of the image that

$$\sum_{\mu=1}^{k} \alpha_\mu = s.$$

For $s = k$, it is a necessary condition that $\alpha_\mu = 1$, because we are interested only in mappings onto K. In this case the mappings are necessarily one-to-one and the question is that of Problem 21.

A mapping of S onto K produces a partition of S; two elements of S belong to the same class, if they have the same image in K (Figure 21). Let T_μ be the subset of S corresponding to the element $y_\mu \in K$; this subset T_μ has order α_μ. Every permutation of the elements of S will give rise to a mapping of S onto K of the same type, since the elements of the classes T_μ will merely be rearranged or possibly exchanged for others—the orders of the classes will be unchanged. Two permutations will give rise to exactly the same mapping of S onto K, if, in going from one to the other, the elements x_i are rearranged only within the classes. The number of one-to-one mappings of S onto itself is $s!$; amongst these are $\alpha_\mu!$ permutations which interchange elements of the class T_μ but leave all the other elements of S unchanged. Hence, there are

$$\alpha_1! \, \alpha_2! \, \alpha_3! \ldots \alpha_k!$$

mappings of S onto itself, which interchange elements only within the different classes of the partition. The number of mappings of S onto K is therefore:

$$P_s(\alpha_1, \alpha_2, \ldots, \alpha_k) = \frac{s!}{\alpha_1! \, \alpha_2! \ldots \alpha_k!} \, ^*.$$

Every mapping of S onto K with the prescribed multiplicity of the images represents an s-sample of K with repetitions.

Problem 27 A teacher distributes 16 library books amongst 4 students. The first is to have four books, the second three, the third six and the last three books. In how many ways can the books be distributed?

Here, the number of mappings of the set of books, S, onto the set of students, K, must be found, with the given multiplicities 4, 3, 6 and 3.

*Note that if $\alpha_1 = \alpha_2 = \ldots = \alpha_k$, i.e., there are no repetitions, we obtain $P_s(1, 1, \ldots, 1) = s! = P_s$.

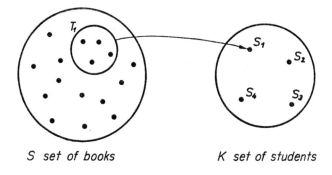

S set of books   K set of students

Fig.22

Problem 28 Let S be a set of order s. How many subsets of S are there of order k $(k \leqslant s)$?

A subset of order k (known as a k-subset of S) divides S into two classes with orders k and $(s-k)$, the first class being the subset under consideration, the second class consisting of the elements of S which do not belong to this subset. With this partition we can associate (see Problem 26) a mapping of the set S onto a set of order 2, with corresponding multiplicities of k and $s-k$. According to Problem 26, therefore, the number of k-subsets of S is

$$P_s(k, s-k) = \frac{s!}{k!\,(s-k)!} = \binom{s}{k}.$$

A k-subset of a set of order s is equivalent to a k-*combination* of s elements without repetitions.

Problem 29 In how many ways can a corporal commanding a squad of six men detail two men for guard duty?

In this problem, we have to find the number of subsets of order 2 of a set of order 6.

Problem 30 Find the number of subsets of a set S.

According to Problem 28, this number is, of course:

$$\sum_{k=0}^{s} \binom{s}{k} = 2^s,$$

if the sets S and $\emptyset$ (i.e. the subsets of order s and 0) are included.

This result may also be obtained as follows:

Let T be a subset of S. We now define the following function on S:

$$f(x_i) = 1 \quad \text{if} \quad x_i \in T,$$
$$f(x_i) = 0 \quad \text{if} \quad x_i \notin T.$$

$f(x_i)$ characterizes a mapping from S to the set $K = \{0, 1\}$. Since the subsets of S can in this way be put into a one-to-one correspondence with the mappings from S to K, it follows from Problem 22 that the number of subsets of S is 2^s.

We can rewrite the result of Problem 30 in the following manner:

$$n(P(S)) = 2^{n(S)}.$$

The order of a finite power set is, therefore, always a power of 2.

1.5 LINEAR INEQUALITIES AND CONVEX POINT SETS

This section deals with infinite point sets* connected with inequalities.

1.5.1 *A linear inequality*

Let the points of n-dimensional space be related to an affine system of coordinates. The linear inequality

$$a_1 x_1 + a_2 x_2 + \ldots + a_n x_n - b \leqslant 0,$$

*Note that in this section we are not talking of sets whose elements are represented by points in a Venn diagram, but of sets whose elements *are* points.

in which not all the coefficients a_i are zero, defines a point set, consisting of all points whose coordinates satisfy the inequality:

$$A = \{p(x_1, x_2, \ldots, x_n) \,|\, a_1 x_1 + a_2 x_2 + \ldots + a_n x_n - b \leq 0\}.$$

We shall first consider these inequalities when n is small. For $n = 1$, the set A corresponding to the linear inequality

$$a_1 x_1 - b \leq 0, \ (a_1 \neq 0),$$

is a ray (Figure 23) whose end-point is given by the equation $a_1 x_1 - b = 0$.

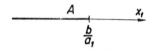

Fig.23

For $n = 2$, the set A corresponding to the linear inequality

$$a_1 x_1 + a_2 x_2 - b \leq 0, \ (a_1, a_2) \neq (0, 0),$$

is a half-plane (Figure 24) whose defining line is given by the equation $a_1 x_1 + a_2 x_2 - b = 0$

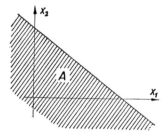

Fig.24

For $n = 3$, the set A corresponding to the linear inequality

$$a_1 x_1 + a_2 x_2 + a_3 x_3 - b \leqslant 0, (a_1, a_2, a_3) \neq (0, 0, 0),$$

is a half-space (Figure 25) bounded by the plane with equation $a_1 x_1 + a_2 x_2 + a_3 x_3 - b = 0$.

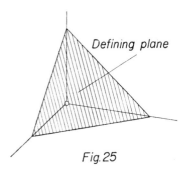

Defining plane

Fig. 25

Definition The set of points whose coordinates satisfy the linear inequality

$$a_1 x_1 + a_2 x_2 + \ldots + a_n x_n - b \leqslant 0,$$

is called a closed half-space of n-dimensional space. We can also speak of it as the solution set of the inequality. The equation $a_1 x_1 + a_2 x_2 + \ldots + a_n x_n - b = 0$ characterizes the *defining hyperplane* of this half-space.

1.5.2 *Systems of linear inequalities. The polyhedral set*

We shall now consider various linear inequalities and the point sets they define. We shall wish to refer to the *solution set of the corresponding system of linear inequalities*. In order to clarify somewhat the different possibilities for the solution set, we shall begin by considering a few simple examples.

For $n = 1$, we consider the system of two inequalities:

$$\left. \begin{array}{l} a_{11} x_1 - b_1 \leqslant 0, a_{11} \neq 0 \\ a_{21} x_1 - b_2 \leqslant 0, a_{21} \neq 0 \end{array} \right\}.$$

If A_1 and A_2 are the solution sets of the individual inequalities (i.e. the point sets in the one-dimensional affine space), the solution set of the system is given by $L = A_1 \cap A_2$. Three types of solution set can arise and these are shown in the following examples:

(1)
$$\{p(x_1) \mid x_1 - 4 \leqslant 0\} = A_1,$$
$$\{p(x_1) \mid -x_1 + 2 \leqslant 0\} = A_2.$$

In this case, the set $L = A_1 \cap A_2$ is bounded (Figure 26).

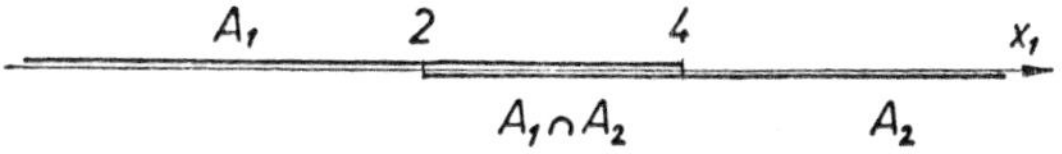

Fig. 26

(2)
$$\{p(x_1) \mid x_1 - 4 \leqslant 0\} = A_1,$$
$$\{p(x_1) \mid x_1 - 2 \leqslant 0\} = A_2.$$

Here, the set $L = A_1 \cap A_2$ is unbounded (Figure 27).

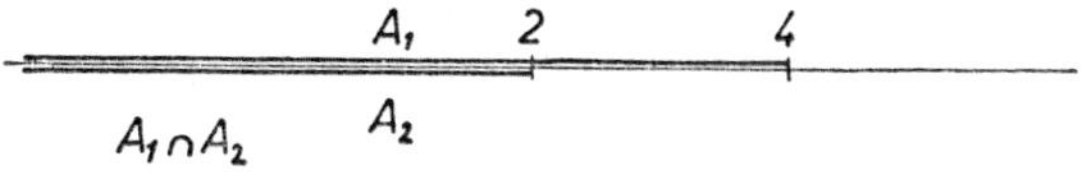

Fig. 27

(3)
$$\{p(x_1) \mid x_1 - 1 \leqslant 0\} = A_1,$$
$$\{p(x_1) \mid -x_1 + 2 \leqslant 0\} = A_2.$$

In this case, the set $L = A_1 \cap A_2 = \emptyset$ is empty (Figure 28).

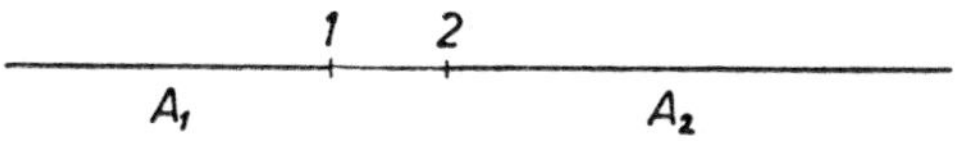

Fig. 28

For $n = 2$, a system of two inequalities,

$$\left. \begin{array}{l} a_{11}x_1 + a_{12}x_2 - b_1 \leqslant 0, (a_{11}, a_{12}) \neq (0, 0) \\ a_{21}x_1 + a_{22}x_2 - b_2 \leqslant 0, (a_{21}, a_{22}) \neq (0, 0) \end{array} \right\},$$

always defines an angle, a parallel strip or a half-plane.

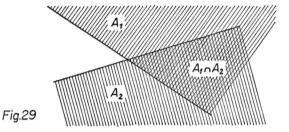

Fig.29

Figure 29 illustrates how two inequalities can define an angle.

For a system of three inequalities, it can be easily seen that when $n = 1$ only three types of solution set can occur, the same possibilities as occurred in the case of systems with two inequalities. Figure 30 shows three of the possibilities that arise when $n = 2$.

Problem 31   Find all the types of solution set that can arise for $n = 2$.

In part (1) of Figure 30, the set L is bounded, in part (2) it is unbounded and in part (3) it is the empty set.

We shall now proceed to deal with the general case of a system of m inequalities in n variables:

$$\left.\begin{array}{l} a_{11}x_1 + a_{12}x_2 + \ldots + a_{1n}x_n - b_1 \leqslant 0 \\ a_{21}x_1 + a_{22}x_2 + \ldots + a_{2n}x_n - b_2 \leqslant 0 \\ \quad\cdot \qquad\quad \cdot \qquad\quad \cdot \qquad\quad \cdot \\ \quad\cdot \qquad\quad \cdot \qquad\quad \cdot \qquad\quad \cdot \\ a_{m1}x_1 + a_{m2}x_2 + \ldots + a_{mn}x_n - b_m \leqslant 0 \end{array}\right\}.$$

Again, not all a_{ik} should be zero for any given i.

The i-th inequality defines a half-space A_i ($i = 1, 2, \ldots, m$). The solution set of the system of inequalities is the intersection set

$$L = A_1 \cap A_2 \cap A_3 \cap \ldots \cap A_m = \bigcap_{i=1}^{m} A_i$$

Definition   The intersection of a finite number of half-spaces is called a *polyhedral set*.

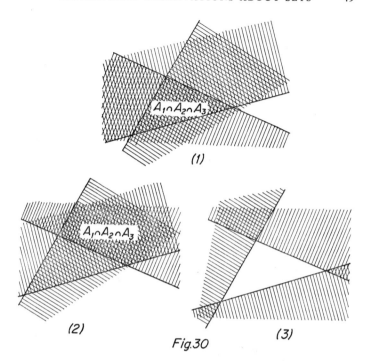

Fig.30

Our notation for the system of m linear inequalities may be simplified by the use of matrices. We write:

$$\begin{pmatrix} a_{11} \, a_{12} \, \ldots \, a_{1n} \\ a_{21} \, a_{22} \qquad a_{2n} \\ \cdot \quad \cdot \qquad \cdot \\ \cdot \quad \cdot \qquad \cdot \\ a_{m1} \, a_{m2} \, \ldots \, a_{mn} \end{pmatrix} = \mathbf{S}, \begin{pmatrix} b_1 \\ b_2 \\ \cdot \\ \cdot \\ b_m \end{pmatrix} = \mathbf{b}, \begin{pmatrix} x_1 \\ x_2 \\ \cdot \\ \cdot \\ x_m \end{pmatrix} = \mathbf{x}.$$

The system of inequalities may then be written as follows:

$$\mathbf{Sx} \leqslant \mathbf{b}.$$

We now arrive at an important property of polyhedral sets.

Definition   A point set M in an n-dimensional affine space is said to be *convex* if for every two points p, $q \in M$, the whole segment $[p, q]$ is a subset of M.

Let us consider, as an example, the set of points contained inside a simply closed plane polygon, i.e., a polygon that does not intersect itself. Figure 31 shows an example of both a convex and a non-convex set.

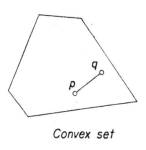
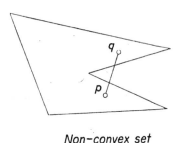

Convex set   Non-convex set

Fig. 31

In order to show whether or not a point set is convex, we use an analytical method. The point v with the position vector

$$\mathbf{v} = \mathbf{p} + \lambda(\mathbf{q} - \mathbf{p})$$

is located on $[p, q]$ if, and only if, $0 \leqslant \lambda \leqslant 1$. The position vectors of the points of $[p, q]$ may therefore be written as follows:

$$\mathbf{v} = \mathbf{p} + \lambda(\mathbf{q} - \mathbf{p}) = (1 - \lambda)\mathbf{p} + \lambda\mathbf{q} \text{ with } 0 \leqslant \lambda \leqslant 1,$$

or

$$\mathbf{v} = \lambda_1 \mathbf{p} + \lambda_2 \mathbf{q} \text{ with } \lambda_1, \lambda_2 \geqslant 0 \text{ and } \lambda_1 + \lambda_2 = 1.$$

The convexity of a point set L in an n-dimensional affine space may now be characterized as follows:

L is a convex set if whenever $p \in L$ and $q \in L$, and

$$\mathbf{v} = \lambda_1 \mathbf{p} + \lambda_2 \mathbf{q} \text{ with } \lambda_1, \lambda_2 \geqslant 0 \text{ and } \lambda_1 + \lambda_2 = 1,$$

it is always true that $v \in L$.

We shall now prove several theorems about convexity.

Theorem 1 If the intersection of a finite number of convex point sets A_i contains two distinct points, it is itself a convex point set.

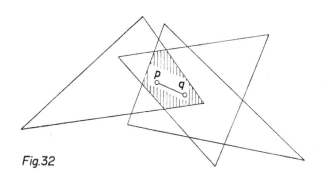

Fig.32

Proof According to the hypothesis, $A_1 \cap A_2 \cap \ldots \cap A_m$ contains at least two points which we shall denote by p and q. Since all A_i are convex, it follows (Figure 32) that

$$[p, q] \subset A_i (i = 1, 2, \ldots, m).$$

This means that

$$[p, q] \subset A_1 \cap A_2 \cap \ldots \cap A_m.$$

Since this result is true for every point pair of the intersection, the convexity of the intersection set is proved.

Theorem 2 A half-space is a convex point set.

Proof A half-space is defined by a linear inequality

$$\mathbf{S}\mathbf{x} \leqslant \mathbf{b} \quad (m \geqslant 1).$$

If p and q are points of this half-space, their position vectors $\mathbf{p}$ and $\mathbf{q}$ satisfy the inequalities

$$\mathbf{S}\mathbf{p} \leqslant \mathbf{b} \quad \text{and} \quad \mathbf{S}\mathbf{q} \leqslant \mathbf{b}.$$

The position vector $\mathbf{v}$ of a random point v on the connecting segment $[p, q]$ can be given in the form

$$\mathbf{v} = \lambda_1\,\mathbf{p} + \lambda_2\,\mathbf{q} \text{ where } \lambda_1, \lambda_2 \geqslant 0 \text{ and } \lambda_1 + \lambda_2 = 1.$$

Then

$$\mathbf{Sv} = \lambda_1\,\mathbf{Sp} + \lambda_2\,\mathbf{Sq} \leqslant (\lambda_1 + \lambda_2)\mathbf{b} = \mathbf{b},$$

which means that v is in the given half-space.

From Theorems 1 and 2 we immediately obtain:

Theorem 3   Every polyhedral set is a convex point set.

The polyhedral sets form the basis of an important method of Operational Research, known as *Linear Programming*. In this method, the maximum or the minimum of a linear function of n variables subject to certain secondary conditions must be found. Generally, the secondary conditions are given by a system of m linear inequalities in the n variables. The solution of the problem results from the investigation of the variation of a linear function over a polyhedral set. However, the discussion of this problem lies outside the scope of this book.

Problem 32   The points $a\,(2, 0)$, $b\,(0, 2)$, $c\,(-2, 0)$ and $d\,(0,\ -2)$ of the plane are the corners of a square. What system of inequalities describes the set of points inside the square?

Problem 33   Graph the following plane point sets

$$A = \{p(x_1, x_2) \,|\, (x_1 - 2x_2 + 4)(3x_1 + x_2 - 9) \geqslant 0\},$$
$$B = \{p(x_1, x_2) \,|\, (2x_1 + 3x_2 - 6)(x_1 - 2x_2 + 4)(3x_1 + x_2 - 9)$$
$$\leqslant 0\},$$
$$C = \{p(x_1, x_2) \,|\, \sin x_1 - \sin x_2 > 0; 0 \leqslant x_1 \leqslant 2\pi;$$
$$0 \leqslant x_2 \leqslant 2\pi\}.$$

Problem 34   Describe the following point sets in the plane:

$D = \{p(x_1, x_2) \mid x_1^2 + x_2^2 \leqslant 25; \; x_1 - x_2^2 \geqslant 0\},$

$E = \{p(x_1, x_2) \mid x_1^2 + x_2^2 \leqslant 25; \; x_1 - x_2^2 \geqslant 0; \; x_1, x_2 \in N\},$

$F = \{p(x_1, x_2) \mid x_1^2 + x_2^2 \leqslant 25; \; x_1 - x_2^2 \geqslant 0; \; x_1^2, x_2^2 \in N\},$

$G = \{p(x_1, x_2) \mid 2x_1 + 3x_2 - 6 \geqslant 0; \; 3x_1 + x_2 - 9 \leqslant 0;$
$\qquad\qquad x_1 - 2x_2 + 4 \geqslant 0; \; x_1, x_2 \in N\}.$

Problem 35 Find the maximum and the minimum of the function $f(x_1, x_2) = x_1 + 2x_2 + 10$ on the sets D, E, F, and G of Problem 34.

Note that the lines corresponding to different values of $f(x_1, x_2)$ are parallel.

AN INTRODUCTION TO BOOLEAN ALGEBRA

In Section 1.2 we used finite power sets in order to develop the basic laws of the algebra of sets. We shall now consider a random set, whose elements are denoted by capital letters. Two operations are defined on this set, called *union* and *intersection*, and denoted by the symbols $\cup$ and $\cap$, respectively. In analogy with the rules established above, we postulate the following axioms:

Ia. $A \cup B = B \cup A$,   Ib. $A \cap B = B \cap A$.

Hence, the two operations are commutative.

IIa. $A \cup (B \cap C)$ IIb. $A \cap (B \cup C)$
$= (A \cup B) \cap (A \cup C)$, $= (A \cap B) \cup (A \cap C)$.

Either of the two operations is distributive over the other.

IIIa. There is a zero element O having the property that

$$A \cup O = O \cup A = A$$

for every A.
O is the identity element for the operation $\cup$.

IIIb. There is a unit element E having the property that

$$A \cap E = E \cap A = A$$

for every A.
E is the identity element for the operation $\cap$.

Corresponding to every element A there is an element A' such that

IVa. $A \cup A' = E$,   IVb. $A \cap A' = O.$*

We call the element A' a *complement* of A.

*Compared with section 1.2, the symbols $\emptyset$, U have been changed to O, E.

54

Definition   A set $\Omega = \{A, B, \ldots\}$ which is closed under two operations, denoted by $\cup$ and $\cap$, is said to be a *Boolean lattice* if the axioms I, II, III and IV are all satisfied. The theory resulting from this system of axioms is called *Boolean algebra*.*

The axioms I, II, III, IV determine an abstract structure. If the elements A, B, C, ... and the operations $\cup$ and $\cap$ are given a definite meaning, then one obtains a model for the structure. We have already dealt with one example: the power set $P(U)$ of a set U is a Boolean lattice under the operations of set union and set intersection.

Problem 36   Let $\Omega = \{1, 2, 3, 5, 6, 10, 15, 30\}$. For $A, B \in \Omega$, $A \cup B$ is defined to be the least common multiple of A and B (LCM) and $A \cap B$ to be the greatest common divisor of A and B (GCD). Show that $[\Omega, \cup, \cap]$ is a Boolean lattice.

Hint: Note that

$$\Omega = \{A \mid A = 2^{\alpha_1}3^{\alpha_2}5^{\alpha_3}, \alpha_j = 0, 1\}$$

and

$$A \cup B = 2^{\max(\alpha_1,\beta_1)}3^{\max(\alpha_2,\beta_2)}5^{\max(\alpha_3,\beta_3)},$$
$$A \cap B = 2^{\min(\alpha_1,\beta_1)}3^{\min(\alpha_2,\beta_2)}5^{\min(\alpha_3,\beta_3)}.$$

As shown in Section 1.3.3, the axioms I to IV may be easily verified. This lattice is isomorphic to the lattice of the power set of the set $U = \{2, 3, 5\}$.

By drawing conclusions from the axioms, we obtain theorems which are valid for all models. Given any model satisfying our set of axioms, then every theorem will contain a specific statement about that model. If, on the other hand, we work from the start with a particular model, then the results we obtain cannot be transferred to other Boolean lattices without further ado.

So far, no uniform notation has been adopted for the

---

*Boolean algebra goes back to a paper by G. Boole, *The Mathematical Analysis of Logic*, published in 1847.

theory of Boolean lattices. The following notations exist side by side:

$$A \cup B \qquad A \cap B \qquad A' \text{ or } \overline{A}$$
$$A + B \qquad A \cdot B \qquad A' \text{ or } \overline{A}$$
$$A \vee B \qquad A \wedge B \qquad \sim A \text{ or } \neg A$$

The symbols shown in the third line are those used in formal logic. The symbols in the second line are more often used in the algebra of switching circuits.

2.2 SOME THEOREMS OF BOOLEAN ALGEBRA

If, in a Boolean lattice, we interchange the two operations $\cup$ and $\cap$ and, at the same time, the two elements O and E, the set of axioms Ia, IIa, IIIa, IVa is transformed into the set of axioms Ib, IIb, IIIb, IVb and vice versa. In a Boolean lattice these two interchanges define a duality. Since the whole system of axioms is self-dual, we obtain immediately the following theorem:

Principle of Duality Any theorem which can be derived from the axioms remains true if the symbols $\cup$ and $\cap$, and the elements O and E are simultaneously interchanged throughout the statement of the theorem.

We shall now proceed with the proof of some formal relations. Where these consist of two dual parts we shall, in view of the principle of duality, need to prove only one of them. In the proofs we shall indicate the axioms and theorems used at each stage of the argument.

Theorem 1 The two identity elements O and E are unique.

Proof We show the uniqueness of O. If O_1 and O_2 are two zero elements, it follows that:

$$\left. \begin{array}{l} O_2 \cup O_1 = O_2 \\ O_1 \cup O_2 = O_1 \end{array} \right\}; \; O_2 \cup O_1 = O_1 \cup O_2 \Rightarrow O_1 = O_2.$$

$$\underbrace{}_{\text{IIIa}} \qquad \underbrace{}_{\text{Ia}}$$

Theorem 2   For every element A of a Boolean lattice,

$$A \cup A = A \quad \text{and} \quad A \cap A = A.$$

Nothing like this exists in conventional algebra. All elements are said to be *idempotent* with respect to both operations.

Proof   We shall prove the statement $A \cup A = A$.

$$A = \underbrace{A \cup O}_{\text{IIIa}} = \underbrace{A \cup (A \cap A')}_{\text{IVb}} = \underbrace{(A \cup A) \cap (A \cup A')}_{\text{IIa}}$$
$$= \underbrace{(A \cup A) \cap E}_{\text{IVa}} = \underbrace{A \cup A}_{\text{IIIb}}.$$

Axioms IIIa and IIIb link every element A to O by $\cup$, and to E by $\cap$. The next theorem links A by $\cup$ to E and by $\cap$ to O.

Theorem 3   For all elements A,

$$A \cup E = E \quad \text{and} \quad A \cap O = O.$$

Proof   We shall prove the statement $A \cup E = E$.

$$E = \underbrace{A \cup A'}_{\text{IVa}} = \underbrace{A \cup (A' \cap E)}_{\text{IIIb}} = \underbrace{(A \cup A') \cap (A \cup E)}_{\text{IIa}}$$
$$= \underbrace{E \cap (A \cup E)}_{\text{IVa}} = \underbrace{A \cup E}_{\text{IIIb}}.$$

Theorem 4 (laws of absorption)   The following relations hold for all elements A and B:

$$A \cup (A \cap B) = A \quad \text{and} \quad A \cap (A \cup B) = A.$$

Proof   We shall prove the statement $A \cup (A \cap B) = A$.

$$A = \underbrace{A \cap E}_{\text{IIIb}} = \underbrace{A \cap (E \cup B)}_{\text{Th. 2}} = \underbrace{(A \cap E) \cup (A \cap B)}_{\text{IIb}} = \underbrace{A \cup (A \cap B)}_{\text{IIIb}}.$$

Theorem 5   The following implications are valid in a Boolean lattice:

$$\left.\begin{array}{l} A \cup X = A \cup Y \\ A' \cup X = A' \cup Y \end{array}\right\} \Rightarrow X = Y$$

and

$$\left.\begin{array}{l} A \cap X = A \cap Y \\ A' \cap X = A' \cap Y \end{array}\right\} \Rightarrow X = Y.$$

Proof   We shall prove the first implication.

$$(A \cup X) \cap (A' \cup X) = \underbrace{(A \cap A')}_{\text{IIa}} \cup X = \underbrace{O \cup X}_{\text{IVb}} = X.$$

Similarly:

$$(A \cup Y) \cap (A' \cup Y) = (A \cap A') \cup Y = O \cup Y = Y.$$

It follows, therefore, from our assumptions, that

$$(A \cup X) \cap (A' \cup X) = (A \cup Y) \cap (A' \cup Y) \Rightarrow X = Y.$$

Theorem 6   The following implication is valid:

$$\left.\begin{array}{l} A \cup X = A \cup Y \\ A \cap X = A \cap Y \end{array}\right\} \Rightarrow X = Y.$$

This theorem is self-dual.

Proof

$$A' \cup (A \cap X) = \underbrace{(A' \cup A)}_{\text{IIa}} \cap (A' \cup X) = \underbrace{E \cap (A' \cup X)}_{\text{IVa}} = \underbrace{A' \cup X}_{\text{IIIb}}.$$

It follows from our assumptions that

$$A' \cup (A \cap X) = A' \cup (A \cap Y) \Rightarrow A' \cup X = A' \cup Y.$$

We now have:

$$\left.\begin{array}{l} A \cup X = A \cup Y \\ A \cap X = A \cap Y \end{array}\right\} \Rightarrow \left.\begin{array}{l} A \cup X = A \cup Y \\ A' \cup X = A' \cup Y \end{array}\right\}\underbrace{\Rightarrow}_{\text{Th.5}} X = Y.$$

Theorem 7   The two operations are associative, i.e. for all A, B and C,

$$A \cup (B \cup C) = (A \cup B) \cup C \quad \text{and} \quad A \cap (B \cap C) = (A \cap B) \cap C.$$

Proof   We shall use Theorem 5 to prove the first statement. We set:

$$X = A \cup (B \cup C); \qquad Y = (A \cup B) \cup C.$$

Then:

$$A \cap X = A \cap [A \cup (B \cup C)] \underset{\text{Th.4}}{=} A,$$

$$A \cap Y = A \cap [(A \cup B) \cup C] \underset{\text{IIb}}{=} [A \cap (A \cup B)] \cup (A \cap C)$$

$$\underset{\text{Th.4}}{=} A \cup (A \cap C) \underset{\text{Th.4}}{=} A,$$

$$A' \cap X = A' \cap [A \cup (B \cup C)] \underset{\text{IIb}}{=} (A' \cap A) \cup [A' \cap (B \cup C)]$$

$$\underset{\text{IVb}}{=} 0 \cup [A' \cap (B \cup C)] = A' \cap (B \cup C),$$

$$A' \cap Y = A' \cap [(A \cup B) \cup C] \underset{\text{IIb}}{=} [A' \cap (A \cup B)] \cup (A' \cap C)$$

$$\underset{\text{IIb}}{=} [(A' \cap A) \cup (A' \cap B)] \cup (A' \cap C)$$

$$\underset{\text{IVb}}{=} [0 \cup (A' \cap B)] \cup (A' \cap C) \underset{\text{IIIa}}{=} (A' \cap B) \cup (A' \cap C)$$

$$\underset{\text{IIb}}{=} A' \cap (B \cup C).$$

Hence,

$$A \cap X = A \cap Y \quad \text{and} \quad A' \cap X = A' \cap Y,$$

and so, using Theorem 5, we conclude that $X = Y$.

In the axioms IVa and IVb we only postulated that every element A is associated with some complementary element A'. We did not insist that the complement should be uniquely defined. We shall now prove:

Theorem 8 For each element A the element A' is uniquely defined.

Proof Suppose that A has two complements, A_1' and A_2'. Then, by IVa and IVb:

$$A \cup A_1' = E, \quad A \cup A_2' = E,$$
$$A \cap A_1' = O, \quad A \cap A_2' = O.$$

It now follows directly from Theorem 6 that $A_1' = A_2'$.

Theorem 9 For all A, $(A')' = A$.

Proof The following relations follow from the definition of $(A')'$:

$$A' \cup (A')' = E \quad \text{and} \quad A' \cap (A')' = O.$$

These relations are, however, satisfied when $(A')'$ is replaced by A. Since, by Theorem 8, the complement is uniquely defined, it follows that $(A')' = A$.

Theorem 10 $O' = E$ and $E' = O$.

Proof According to IIIa and IIIb,

$$E \cup O = E \quad \text{and} \quad E \cap O = O.$$

It follows directly from the uniqueness of the complement that

$$O' = E \quad \text{and} \quad E' = O.$$

Theorem 11 (de Morgan's Laws) The following laws hold for the formation of the complements of intersections and unions:

$$(A \cup B)' = A' \cap B' \quad \text{and} \quad (A \cap B)' = A' \cup B'.$$

Proof

$$(A \cap B) \cap (A' \cup B') = \underset{\text{IIb}}{=} [(A \cap B) \cap A'] \cup [(A \cap B) \cap B']$$

$$\underset{\text{Ib}}{=} [A' \cap (A \cap B)] \cup [(A \cap B) \cap B']$$

$$\underset{\text{Th.7}}{=} [(A' \cap A) \cap B] \cup [A \cap (B \cap B')]$$

$$\underset{\text{IVb}}{=} (O \cap B) \cup (A \cap O) \underset{\text{Th.3}}{=} O \cup O \underset{\text{IIIa}}{=} O.$$

Hence,

$$(A \cap B) \cap (A' \cup B') = O. \tag{1}$$

On the other hand,

$$(A \cap B) \cup (A' \cup B') \underset{\text{Ia}}{=} (A' \cup B') \cup (A \cap B)$$

$$\underset{\text{IIa}}{=} [(A' \cup B') \cup A] \cap [(A' \cup B') \cup B]$$

$$\underset{\text{Ia, Th.7}}{=} [B' \cup (A \cup A')] \cap [A' \cup (B \cup B')]$$

$$\underset{\text{IVa}}{=} (B' \cup E) \cap (A' \cup E) \underset{\text{Th.3}}{=} E \cap E \underset{\text{IIIb}}{=} E.$$

It is therefore true that

$$(A \cap B) \cup (A' \cup B') = E. \tag{2}$$

In view of Theorem 8, the equations (1) and (2) imply that $A' \cup B'$ is the complement of $A \cap B$, i.e.,

$$(A \cap B)' = A' \cup B'.$$

Problem 37 Prove, by means of induction, the following generalizations of de Morgan's Laws:

$$(A_1 \cup A_2 \cup \ldots \cup A_n)' = A_1' \cap A_2' \cap \ldots \cap A_n',$$
$$(A_1 \cap A_2 \cap \ldots \cap A_n)' = A_1' \cup A_2' \cup \ldots \cup A_n'.$$

Using de Morgan's Laws and Theorems 8 and 10 we can obtain the following equivalences:

$$A \cup B = B \cup A \quad \Leftrightarrow \quad A' \cap B' = B' \cap A',$$
$$A \cap B = B \cap A \quad \Leftrightarrow \quad A' \cup B' = B' \cup A',$$
$$\begin{aligned} A \cap (B \cup C) & \\ = (A \cap B) \cup (A \cap C) \end{aligned} \Leftrightarrow \begin{aligned} A' \cup (B' \cap C') & \\ = (A' \cup B') \cap (A' \cup C'), \end{aligned}$$
$$A \cup O = O \cup A = A \quad \Leftrightarrow \quad A' \cap E = E \cap A' = A'.$$
$$A \cup A' = E \quad \Leftrightarrow \quad A \cap A' = O.$$

Problem 38 Show that the elements O and E together with the operations $\cup$ and $\cap$ form a Boolean lattice and write down the combination tables for both operations.

In Chapter 5 we shall deal in detail with the algebra of circuits. There, the simplest Boolean lattice, consisting of only the elements O and E, occurs naturally. Conventionally, in the algebra of circuits, the elements are denoted by lower case letters, the letter O is replaced by 0 and E by 1. The symbol $\cup$ is replaced by $+$ and the symbol $\cap$ by ., and this dot is usually omitted between factors as in ordinary algebra.

Problem 39 Rewrite axioms I to IV and the theorems derived therefrom, in the notation of the algebra of circuits.

In order to get used to this other notation, we shall now give examples of how several expressions can be simplified.

Example 1
$$x + x'y = \underbrace{(x + x')(x + y)}_{\text{IIa}} = \underbrace{1 \,.\, (x + y)}_{\text{IVa}} = \underbrace{x + y}_{\text{IIIb}}.$$

Example 2
$$\begin{aligned}
ux + vx' + uv &= ux(v + v') + vx'(u + u') + uv(x + x')\\
&= uvx + uv'x + uvx' + u'vx' + uvx + uvx'\\
&= uvx + uv'x + uvx' + u'vx'\\
&= ux(v + v') + vx'(u + u')\\
&= ux + vx'.
\end{aligned}$$

Here, the idempotency rule was used, whereby a summand occurring several times need be written only once.

Example 3

$$ux + vx' = ux + vx' + uv = (u+x')(v+x),$$

because $xx' = 0$.

Example 4

$$\begin{aligned}
(a+b)(b+c)(c+a) &= [(a+b)(b+c)](c+a) \\
&= (b+ac)(c+a) \\
&= bc + ba + acc + aac \\
&= ab + bc + ca.
\end{aligned}$$

Problem 40   Prove the relation

$$a_1(a_1' + a_2)(a_1' + a_2' + a_3) \ldots (a_1' + a_2' + \ldots + a_{n-1}' + a_n)$$
$$= a_1 a_2 \ldots a_n,$$

using the method of induction, and write down its dual.

The two distributive laws play an important role in the simplification of terms. However, the use of the operators $+$ and $\cdot$ from conventional algebra has the drawback that it encourages us to think mainly of distributive law IIb and possible simplifications using law IIa are not obvious. This difficulty may be overcome by use of the dual of the term to be simplified. The method is demonstrated in the following example, the simplification of

$$w = \underbrace{bc + ab'cd + cd'}_{u} + \underbrace{ac' + a'bc' + b'c'd'}_{v}.$$

The dual term $D(u)$ to u reads:

$$\begin{aligned}
D(u) &= (b+c)(a+b'+c+d)(c+d') = (c+bd')(a+b'+c+d) \\
&= c + bd'(a+b'+d) = c + abd'.
\end{aligned}$$

When multiplying out the brackets, we have here used Theorem 7. This simplification of $D(u)$ gives us for u:

$$u = c(a+b+d').$$

In the same way we can transform the dual $D(v)$ to v:

$$\begin{aligned}
D(v) &= (a+c')(a'+b+c')(b'+c'+d') \\
&= [(c'+a(a'+b)]\,(b'+c'+d') \\
&= (c'+ab)(b'+c'+d') \\
&= c'+ab(b'+d') = c'+abd'.
\end{aligned}$$

Thus $v = c'(a+b+d')$, and we obtain finally for w:

$$w = u+v = a+b+d'.$$

We shall end this section by noting that the implication

$$A \subset B \Leftrightarrow A \cap B = A$$

enables a partial ordering to be introduced into every Boolean lattice; the results of Section 1.3.4 carry over completely from the algebra of sets into Boolean algebra. It should again be stressed that a partial ordering represents a reflexive, anti-symmetric and transitive relation. We shall use this in our investigation into finite Boolean lattices.

Problem 41   What is the relevance of the relation $A \subset B$ in the Boolean lattice of Problem 36? Draw the associated Hasse diagram.

Definition   A system $[\Omega, \cup, \cap]$ is called a *lattice* if the two operations are commutative and associative and the two absorption laws (Theorem 4) are also valid.

In this definition of a lattice the absorption laws and associativity are postulated, whereas above we have derived them on the basis of our systems of axioms.

If a lattice contains a unit element E and a zero element O, a complement A' may be defined, as has been done in the axioms IVa and IVb. A lattice is called *complemented* if all its elements have complements. If the distributive laws hold in a lattice, it is called a distributive lattice. In this case it can be demonstrated that the complement is uniquely defined. A Boolean lattice now appears as a special kind of lattice, namely, one that is complemented and distributive.

2.3 ADDITIVE FUNCTIONS OVER A BOOLEAN LATTICE. THE INCLUSION AND EXCLUSION FORMULA

The following fundamental properties hold for sets of finite order:

$$n(A) \geqslant 0,$$
$$n(A \cup B) = n(A) + n(B) \quad \text{if} \quad A \cap B = \varnothing.$$

Let us now consider the set of closed polygons in a plane. Each polygon is associated with a set P of points, consisting of the points within the polygon. The point set P may be associated with an area $J(P)$. Obviously if P_1 and P_2 are two polygons then

$$J(P_1 \cup P_2) = J(P_1) + J(P_2), \text{ provided } P_1 \cap P_2 = \varnothing.$$

The function J has therefore the same properties as the order function above.

We shall now leave these examples and consider a general Boolean lattice Ω. Let a real number $\varphi(A)$, which satisfies the following axioms, be associated with every element $A \in \Omega$:

I $\varphi(A) \geqslant 0$,

II $\varphi(A \cup B) = \varphi(A) + \varphi(B)$ if $A \cap B = O$.

Definition If φ fulfils axioms I and II, we say it is a (non-negative) additive function, or a measure function, over the relevant Boolean lattice.*

If the elements of the lattice are sets, φ is called an additive set function.

Order and area are two examples of additive set functions. Volume is another such function. Two further examples will be given later in this book, namely relative frequency and probability.

---

*There is no general agreement as to which set functions ought to be called measures. However, it is more usual to demand that Axiom II should be capable of being extended to cover the union of a countable number of sets, i.e. that $\varphi(\overset{\infty}{\underset{i=1}{\cup}} A_i) = \overset{\infty}{\underset{i=1}{\sum}} \varphi(A_i)$, for disjoint sets A_i.

Several conclusions can be drawn directly from the two postulated properties.

1. From II it follows directly that

$$\varphi(B) = \varphi\,(O \cup B) = \varphi\,(O) + \varphi(B),$$

because $O \cap B = O$. We see therefore that

$$\varphi(O) = 0,$$

or, in other words:

Theorem   The zero element always has measure 0.

2. Suppose $A \subset B$. If A' is the complementary element of A relative to B, then

$$A \cup A' = B \quad \text{and} \quad A \cap A' = O.$$

It follows therefore, in view of II, that

$$\varphi(B) = \varphi(A \cup A') = \varphi(A) + \varphi(A').$$

However, according to I, $\varphi(A) \geqslant 0$, i.e.,

Theorem $A \subset B \Leftrightarrow \varphi(A) \leqslant \varphi(B)$.

3. We see immediately therefore, that if A' is the complement of A relative to B, then

$$\varphi(A') = \varphi(B) - \varphi(A).$$

4. If A, B and C are pair-wise disjoint elements, then

$$\varphi(A \cup B \cup C) = \varphi(A) + \varphi(B) + \varphi(C).$$

By our assumption,

$$A \cap B = B \cap C = C \cap A = O.$$

Hence, it follows that

$$(A \cup B) \cap C = (A \cap C) \cup (A \cap B) = O \cup O = O,$$

that is, $A \cup B$ and C are disjoint. Now using property II twice, we obtain

$$\varphi(A \cup B \cup C) = \varphi((A \cup B) \cup C)$$
$$= \varphi(A \cup B) + \varphi(C)$$
$$= \varphi(A) + \varphi(B) + \varphi(C).$$

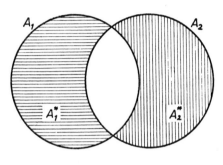

Fig.33

5. We shall now consider two general elements A_1 and A_2 (shown in Figure 33 as point sets). It can easily be verified that the three elements

$$A_1^{\bullet} = A_1 \cap A_2', \ A_2^{\bullet} = A_2 \cap A_1' \text{ and } A_1 \cap A_2$$

are disjoint, and that $A_1 \cup A_2$ can be expressed in the following way:

$$A_1 \cup A_2 = A_1^{\bullet} \cup A_2^{\bullet} \cup (A_1 \cap A_2).$$

Hence, from 4, we can write,

$$\varphi(A_1 \cup A_2) = \varphi(A_1^{\bullet}) + \varphi(A_2^{\bullet}) + \varphi(A_1 \cap A_2).$$

Now using property 3, we obtain,

$$\varphi(A_1 \cup A_2) = \varphi(A_1) - \varphi(A_1 \cap A_2)$$
$$+ \varphi(A_2) - \varphi(A_1 \cap A_2) + \varphi(A_1 \cap A_2),$$

and therefore

$$\varphi(A_1 \cup A_2) = \varphi(A_1) + \varphi(A_2) - \varphi(A_1 \cap A_2).$$

6. This relation can be immediately generalized. Let us first

consider the three elements A_1, A_2, A_3. It follows that

$$
\begin{aligned}
\varphi(A_1 \cup A_2 \cup A_3) &= \varphi\big((A_1 \cup A_2) \cup A_3\big) \\
&= \varphi(A_1 \cup A_2) + \varphi(A_3) - \varphi\big((A_1 \cup A_2) \cap A_3\big) \\
&= \varphi(A_1) + \varphi(A_2) - \varphi(A_1 \cap A_2) + \varphi(A_3) - \\
&\quad - \varphi\big((A_1 \cap A_3) \cup (A_2 \cap A_3)\big) \\
\\
&= \varphi(A_1) + \varphi(A_2) + \varphi(A_3) - \varphi(A_1 \cap A_2) \\
&\quad - \varphi(A_1 \cap A_3) - \varphi(A_2 \cap A_3) \\
&\quad + \varphi\big((A_1 \cap A_3) \cap (A_2 \cap A_3)\big).
\end{aligned}
$$

However,

$$
(A_1 \cap A_3) \cap (A_2 \cap A_3) = A_1 \cap A_2 \cap A_3,
$$

and therefore

$$
\begin{aligned}
\varphi(A_1 \cup A_2 \cup A_3) &= \varphi(A_1) + \varphi(A_2) + \varphi(A_3) - \{\varphi(A_1 \cap A_2) \\
&\quad + \varphi(A_1 \cap A_3) + \varphi(A_2 \cap A_3)\} + \varphi(A_1 \cap A_2 \cap A_3).
\end{aligned}
$$

This is a special case of what is known as the inclusion and exclusion formula which in the case of n elements $A_1, \ldots, A_n$ has the following form

$$
\begin{aligned}
\varphi(A_1 \cup A_2 \cup \ldots \cup A_n) \\
= \sum_{i=1}^{n} \varphi(A_i) - \sum_{i<j}^{n} \varphi(A_i \cap A_j) + \sum_{i<j<k}^{n} \varphi(A_i \cap A_j \cap A_k) \\
- \sum_{i<j<k<s}^{n} \varphi(A_i \cap A_j \cap A_k \cap A_s) + \ldots \\
\ldots + (-1)^{n+1} \varphi(A_1 \cap A_2 \cap \ldots \cap A_n).
\end{aligned} \tag{1}
$$

We shall supply a proof of this by induction. First let us assume that the inclusion and exclusion formula holds for sets of $n-1$ elements:

$$
\begin{aligned}
\varphi(A_1 \cup A_2 \cup \ldots \cup A_{n-1}) \\
= \sum_{i}^{n-1} \varphi(A_i) - \sum_{i<j}^{n-1} \varphi(A_i \cap A_j) + \sum_{i<j<k}^{n-1} \varphi(A_i \cap A_j \cap A_k) \\
- \sum_{i<j<k<s}^{n-1} \varphi(A_i \cap A_j \cap A_k \cap A_s) + \ldots \\
\ldots + (-1)^{n} \varphi(A_1 \cap A_2 \cap \ldots \cap A_{n-1}).
\end{aligned} \tag{2}
$$

It follows from our previous result (equivalent to the case $n = 2$), that

$$
\begin{aligned}
\varphi(A_1 \cup A_2 \cup \ldots \cup A_{n-1} \cup A_n) &= \varphi((A_1 \cup A_2 \cup \ldots \cup A_{n-1}) \cup A_n) \\
&= \varphi(A_1 \cup A_2 \cup \ldots \cup A_{n-1}) + \varphi(A_n) \\
&\quad - \varphi((A_1 \cup A_2 \cup \ldots \cup A_{n-1}) \cap A_n).
\end{aligned} \tag{3}
$$

According to the distributive law, however,

$$
\begin{aligned}
(A_1 \cup A_2 \cup A_3 \cup \ldots \cup A_{n-1}) \cap A_n \\
= (A_1 \cap A_n) \cup (A_2 \cap A_n) \cup \ldots \cup (A_{n-1} \cap A_n).
\end{aligned}
$$

We can now apply the formula for $n-1$ elements to this term:

$$
\begin{aligned}
\varphi((A_1 \cup A_2 \cup \ldots \cup A_{n-1}) \cap A_n) \\
= \sum_{i=1}^{n-1} \varphi(A_i \cap A_n) \\
- \sum_{i<j}^{n-1} \varphi((A_i \cap A_n) \cap (A_j \cap A_n)) \\
+ \sum_{i<j<k}^{n-1} \varphi((A_i \cap A_n) \cap (A_j \cap A_n) \cap (A_k \cap A_n))
\end{aligned}
$$

$$
\cdot
$$

$$
\cdot
$$

$$
\cdot
$$

$$
+ (-1)^n \varphi((A_1 \cap A_n) \cap (A_2 \cap A_n) \cap \ldots \cap (A_{n-1} \cap A_n)).
$$

In view of the properties of associativity, commutativity and idempotency we can write:

$$
\begin{aligned}
(A_i \cap A_n) \cap (A_j \cap A_n) &= A_i \cap A_j \cap A_n, \\
(A_i \cap A_n) \cap (A_j \cap A_n) \cap (A_k \cap A_n) &= A_i \cap A_j \cap A_k \cap A_n,
\end{aligned}
$$

$$
\cdot
$$

$$
\cdot
$$

$$
\cdot
$$

$$
\begin{aligned}
(A_1 \cap A_n) \cap (A_2 \cap A_n) \cap \ldots \cap (A_{n-1} \cap A_n) = \\
A_1 \cap A_2 \cap \ldots \cap A_{n-1} \cap A_n.
\end{aligned}
$$

Hence,

$$\varphi((A_1 \cup A_2 \cup \ldots \cup A_{n-1}) \cap A_n) = \sum_{i=1}^{n-1} \varphi(A_i \cap A_n)$$
$$- \sum_{i<j}^{n-1} \varphi(A_i \cap A_j \cap A_n)$$
$$+ \sum_{i<j<k}^{n-1} \varphi(A_i \cap A_j \cap A_k \cap A_n)$$
$$\cdot$$
$$\cdot$$
$$\cdot$$
$$+ (-1)^n \varphi(A_1 \cap A_2 \cap \ldots$$
$$\ldots \cap A_{n-1} \cap A_n). \quad (4)$$

By substituting (4) and (2) into (3), we obtain the inclusion and exclusion formula for sets of n elements.

For the special case when φ denotes the order of a set, we can obtain an alternative proof by means of combinatorial arguments.

Suppose a universal set U has n subsets $A_1, \ldots, A_n$, and that $p \in A_1 \cup \ldots \cup A_n = U$ is an element belonging to exactly k of these subsets, say, $A_{\sigma 1}, A_{\sigma 2}, \ldots, A_{\sigma k}$. In order to verify the inclusion and exclusion formula it is sufficient to show that the element p is counted exactly once no matter what value k takes. In the first sum of (1), p is counted exactly k times. In the second sum, it is counted as many times as there are ways of selecting two distinct sets from $A_{\sigma 1}, A_{\sigma 2}, \ldots, A_{\sigma k}$, i.e., $\binom{k}{2}$ times. Generally, it occurs $\binom{k}{\rho}$ times in the ρ-th sum. Taking account of the signs, we find that p has been counted

$$f = \binom{k}{1} - \binom{k}{2} + \ldots + (-1)^{k+1} \binom{k}{k}$$

times in the inclusion and exclusion formula.

However,

$$\binom{k}{0} - \binom{k}{1} + \binom{k}{2} - \ldots + (-1)^k \binom{k}{k} = (1-1)^k = 0,$$

and, since $\binom{k}{0} = 1$, it follows that $f = 1$, so that we have established the validity of the inclusion and exclusion formula for the special case of the orders of sets.

Figure 34 shows the case $n = 3, k = 2$.

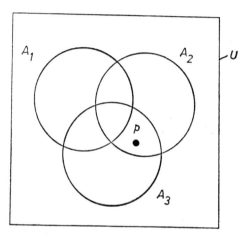

Fig. 34

A further relation can be obtained directly from the inclusion and exclusion formula by dualizing the combinations occurring in it. We can also start the induction proof with

$$\varphi(A_1 \cap A_2) = \varphi(A_1) + \varphi(A_2) - \varphi(A_1 \cup A_2),$$

and obtain

$$\varphi(A_1 \cap A_2 \cap \ldots \cap A_n)$$
$$= \sum_{i=1}^{n} \varphi(A_i) - \sum_{i<j}^{n} \varphi(A_i \cup A_j) + \sum_{i<j<k}^{n} \varphi(A_i \cup A_j \cup A_k) + \ldots$$
$$+ (-1)^{n+1} \varphi(A_1 \cup A_2 \cup \ldots \cup A_n). \tag{5}$$

Problem 42 Prove the dual inclusion and exclusion formula (5) starting from $\varphi(A'_1 \cup A'_2 \cup \ldots \cup A'_n)$.

Hint: Transform $\varphi(A'_1 \cup A'_2 \cup \ldots \cup A'_n)$ using (1) and then rearrange the result, using de Morgan's laws and property 3 for additive functions, in terms of the elements $A_1, A_2, \ldots, A_n$.

So as to simplify our working, we now introduce the abbreviation

$$\sum_{i_1 < i_2 < \ldots < i_k} \varphi(A_{i_1} \cap A_{i_2} \cap \ldots \cap A_{i_k}) = \Phi_k^{(n)}(A),$$

which enables us to write the inclusion and exclusion formula in the form:

$$\varphi(A_1 \cup A_2 \cup \ldots \cup A_n) = \sum_{k=1}^{n} (-1)^{k-1} \Phi_k^{(n)}(A).$$

Problem 43 A_1, A_2 and A_3 are elements of the Boolean lattice Ω. Show that:

$$\varphi(A_1 \cap A'_2 \cap A'_3) = \varphi(A_1) - \varphi(A_1 \cap A_2) - \varphi(A_1 \cap A_3) \\ + \varphi(A_1 \cap A_2 \cap A_3).$$

Hint: Use the relation

$$[A_1 \cap A'_2 \cap A'_3] \cup [(A_1 \cap A_2) \cup (A_1 \cap A_3)] = A_1$$

and note that the two square brackets represent disjoint elements.

Problem 44 Show that

$$\varphi(A_1 \cap A'_2 \cap A'_3) + \varphi(A'_1 \cap A_2 \cap A'_3) + \varphi(A'_1 \cap A'_2 \cap A_3) \\ = \Phi_1^{(3)}(A) - 2\Phi_2^{(3)}(A) + 3\Phi_3^{(3)}(A).$$

Problem 45 (Generalization of Problem 43 from 3 to n elements $A_1, A_2, \ldots, A_n$). The elements

$$K_1 = A_1 \cap A'_2 \cap A'_3 \cap \ldots \cap A'_n, \\ K_2 = A'_1 \cap A_2 \cap A'_3 \cap \ldots \cap A'_n, \ldots$$

are called complete conjunctions of the first order (all n

elements occur in each item while exactly one element is not complemented). Show that

$$\varphi(K_1) = \varphi(A_1) - \sum_{j>1} \varphi(A_1 \cap A_j) + \sum_{\substack{j<k \\ j,k \neq 1}} \varphi(A_1 \cap A_j \cap A_k) - \ldots$$
$$+ (-1)^{n-1} \varphi(A_1 \cap A_2 \cap \ldots \cap A_n).$$

Problem 46   Show that

$$\varphi_1 = \sum_{j=1}^{n} \varphi(K_j) = \sum_{k=0}^{n-1} (-1)^k (n+1) \Phi_{k+1}^{(n)}(A).$$

Problem 47   The element

$$K_{12} = A_1 \cap A_2 \cap A_3' \cap \ldots \cap A_n'$$

is an example of a second-order complete conjunction. Prove the relation

$$\varphi(K_{12}) = \varphi(A_1 \cap A_2) - \sum_{j>2} (A_1 \cap A_2 \cap A_j) + \ldots$$
$$+ (-1)^{n-2} \varphi(A_1 \cap A_2 \cap \ldots \cap A_n).$$

Hint: Set $A_1 \cap A_2 = B$ and use the formula of Problem 45.

Problem 48   Show that

$$\varphi_2 = \sum_{i<j} \varphi(K_{ij}) = \sum_{k=0}^{n-2} (-1)^k \binom{k+2}{k} \Phi_{k+2}^{(n)}(A).$$

The preceding problems indicate a generalization of the inclusion and exclusion formula which will be considered in the next problem.

Problem 49   Find the sum φ_r of the measures of all complete conjunctions of order r of the set $\{A_1, A_2, \ldots, A_n\}$.*

---

*Alternatively one could describe φ_r as the sum of the measures of all intersections of exactly r elements of the set $\{A_1, A_2, \ldots, A_n\}$.

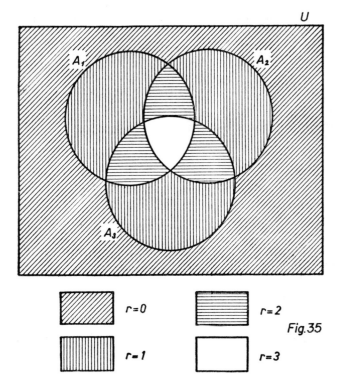

Fig. 35

Figure 35 illustrates a power set lattice for $n = 3$, and shows the sets corresponding to the sums φ_0, φ_1, φ_2, φ_3.

According to the inclusion and exclusion formula,

$$\varphi_0 = \varphi((A_1 \cup A_2 \cup \ldots \cup A_n)')$$
$$= \varphi(U) - \varphi(A_1 \cup A_2 \cup \ldots \cup A_n),$$

that is,

$$\varphi_0 = \varphi(U) - \sum_{k=1}^{n} (-1)^{k-1} \Phi_k^{(n)}(A).$$

By introducing the term $\Phi_0^{(n)}(A) = \varphi(U)$, we can abbreviate this to

$$\varphi_0 = \sum_{k=0}^{n} (-1)^k \Phi_k^{(n)}(A).$$

This is a special case of the general formula by Ch. Jordan,

$$\varphi_r = \sum_{k=0}^{n-r} (-1)^k \binom{r+k}{k} \Phi_{r+k}^{(n)}(A), \tag{6}$$

which solves this problem and which we shall now prove.

Proof We can assume that $r \geqslant 1$, because the formula for $r = 0$ has already been proved. If we limit ourselves to the special case of set order we can proceed in a manner analogous to that of the second proof of the inclusion and exclusion formula.

Let p be an element of the intersection of exactly s of the sets A_i. We shall have to prove that formula (6) takes p into consideration only if $s = r$, and that in this case p is counted exactly once.

In the sum $\Phi_{r+k}^{(n)}(A)$, p is counted exactly as many times as there are ways of selecting $r + k$ distinct sets from $A_{\sigma 1}, \ldots, A_{\sigma s}$,

i.e., $\binom{s}{r+k}$ times. The sum

$$f = \sum_{k=0}^{n-r} (-1)^k \binom{r+k}{k} \binom{s}{r+k}$$

$$= \binom{s}{r}\binom{r}{0} - \binom{s}{r+1}\binom{r+1}{1} + \ldots + (-1)^{n-r}\binom{n}{n-r}\binom{s}{n}$$

tells us, therefore, how many times p has been counted in (6).

Three cases can be distinguished:

(a) $s < r$; $\binom{s}{r+k} = 0$ for all k; i.e. $f = 0$,

(b) $s = r$; $f = \binom{s}{s}\binom{s}{0} = 1$,

(c) $s > r$; we transform the sum f as follows:

$$f = \sum_{k=0}^{n-r} (-1)^k \binom{r+k}{k}\binom{s}{r+k}$$

$$= \sum_{k=0}^{s-r} (-1)^k \frac{(r+k)!}{r!\,k!} \cdot \frac{s!}{(r+k)!(s-r-k)!}$$

$$= \sum_{k=0}^{s-r} (-1)^k \frac{s!}{r!(s-r)!} \cdot \frac{(s-r)!}{k!(s-r-k)!}$$

$$= \binom{s}{r}\sum_{k=0}^{s-r} (-1)^k \binom{s-r}{k} = \binom{s}{r}(1-1)^{s-r} = 0.$$

This proves Jordan's formula for the case of the order function.

Problem 50   Use the results of Problems 43 to 48 to prove Jordan's formula for a general measure function φ.

In Problems 51 to 56, we shall find the area of the shaded regions in the figures. The point sets whose measures are to be calculated are denoted by $P_1, P_2, \ldots, P_6$.

Problem 51 a_1, a_2 and a_3 are the vertices of an equilateral triangle of side $2s$. Two arcs are drawn with centres a_1 and a_2 as shown in Figure 36a.

We introduce two sets A_1 and A_2, sectors of circles with centres a_1 and a_2 respectively. It then follows from the inclusion and exclusion formula that:

$$A(P_1) = A(A_1 \cup A_2) = A(A_1)+A(A_2)-A(A_1 \cap A_2)$$
$$= 2 \cdot \frac{4 \cdot s^2}{6} \pi - (\sqrt{3})s^2.$$

Hence,

$$A(P_1) = \frac{s^2}{3}(4\pi - 3\sqrt{3}).$$

Problem 52   Here, Figure 36a had been completed by an arc over the third side of the equilateral triangle (Figure 36b). We introduce the set A_3, the sector of a circle with centre a_3, and

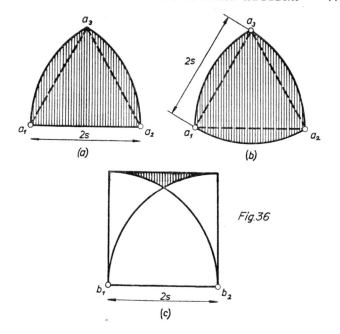

Fig.36

use the inclusion and exclusion formula for three sets:

$$
\begin{aligned}
A(P_2) &= A(A_1 \cup A_2 \cup A_3) \\
&= A(A_1) + A(A_2) + A(A_3) - A(A_1 \cap A_2) \\
&\quad - A(A_1 \cap A_3) - A(A_2 \cap A_3) + A(A_1 \cap A_2 \cap A_3) \\
&= 3\frac{4s^2}{6}\pi - 3(\sqrt{3})s^2 + (\sqrt{3})s^2.
\end{aligned}
$$

Hence,

$$
A(P_2) = 2s^2(\pi - \sqrt{3}).
$$

One can make use of Problem 51 by setting

$$
P_1^* = A_1 \cup A_2 \text{ and } P_1^+ = A_1 \cup A_3.
$$

It then follows that

$$P_2 = P_1^* \cup P_1^+,$$

and it is sufficient to use the inclusion and exclusion formula for two sets.

Problem 53   We introduce as subsets the quadrants B_1 and B_2 of the circles with centres b_1 and b_2 (Figure 36c). Using the inclusion and exclusion formula, as well as the set P_1 of Problem 51, we find that

$$A(B_1 \cup B_2) = A(B_1) + A(B_2) - A(B_1 \cap B_2)$$
$$= 2s^2\pi - A(P_1) = \frac{s^2}{3}(2\pi + 3\sqrt{3}),$$
$$A(P_3) = A((B_1 \cup B_2)') = A(U) - A(B_1 \cup B_2)$$
$$= 4s^2 - A(B_1 \cup B_2),$$
$$A(P_3) = \frac{s^2}{3}(12 - 2\pi - 3\sqrt{3}).$$

Problem 54   We introduce the quadrants C_1 and C_2 as subsets (Figure 37a). It follows from the dual inclusion and exclusion formula that

$$A(P_4) = A(C_1 \cap C_2)$$
$$= 2\frac{4\pi s^2}{4} - A(C_1 \cup C_2) = 2\pi s^2 - 4s^2.$$

Hence,

$$A(P_4) = 2s^2 \ (\pi - 2).$$

Problem 55   In order to calculate the area of the region shaded in Figure 37b, we use the subsets P_1^* and P_1^+ (see Problem 52), marked in the figure at their bases. By means of the dual inclusion and exclusion formula, and using $A(P_1)$ and $A(P_3)$, we find

$$A(P_5) = A(P_1^* \cap P_1^+)$$
$$= A(P_1^*) + A(P_1^+) - A(P_1^* \cup P_1^+)$$
$$= 2A(P_1) - [A(U) - 2A(P_3)].$$

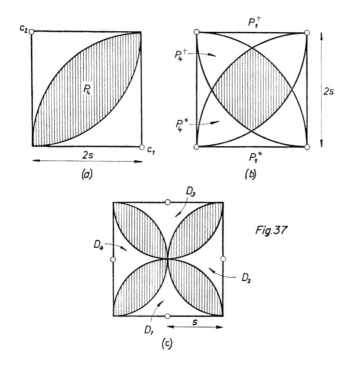

Fig. 37

Hence,

$$A(P_5) = \frac{4s^2}{3}(\pi + 3 - 3\sqrt{3}).$$

It would be equally possible to use the two sets P_4^* and P_4^+.

Problem 56 The area of a single leaf in Figure 37c is (by similarity) a quarter of the area of P_4. Hence,

$$A(P_6) = A(P_4) = 2s^2(\pi - 2).$$

This area could also be calculated using the four semicircular sets D_1, D_2, D_3 and D_4, marked in Figure 37c at their bases. We find, for the union of these sets:

$$
\begin{aligned}
4s^2 &= A(D_1 \cup D_2 \cup D_3 \cup D_4) \\
&= A(D_1) + A(D_2) + A(D_3) + A(D_4) \\
&\quad - A(D_1 \cap D_2) - \underbrace{A(D_1 \cap D_3)}_{\varnothing} - A(D_1 \cap D_4) \\
&\quad - A(D_2 \cap D_3) - \underbrace{A(D_2 \cap D_4)}_{\varnothing} - A(D_3 \cap D_4) \\
&\quad + \underbrace{A(D_1 \cap D_2 \cap D_3)}_{\varnothing} + \underbrace{A(D_1 \cap D_2 \cap D_4)}_{\varnothing} \\
&\quad + \underbrace{A(D_1 \cap D_3 \cap D_4)}_{\varnothing} + \underbrace{A(D_2 \cap D_3 \cap D_4)}_{\varnothing} \\
&\quad - \underbrace{A(D_1 \cap D_2 \cap D_3 \cap D_4)}_{\varnothing}.
\end{aligned}
$$

Since

$$A(P_6) = A(D_1 \cap D_2) + A(D_2 \cap D_3) + A(D_3 \cap D_4) + A(D_4 \cap D_1),$$

it follows that

$$A(P_6) = 2s^2\pi - 4s^2 = 2s^2(\pi - 2).$$

Problem 57 If a spherical triangle, D, has angles α, β and γ, then its area is given by

$$\varphi(D) = \pi - (\alpha + \beta + \gamma).$$

Derive this relation by means of the inclusion and exclusion formula.

The following point sets on the sphere may be used:

(a) A_1, B_1, C_1, hemispherical sets on the sides of the triangle.
(b) A_2, B_2, C_2, lune sets over the angles of the triangle.

It should be pointed out that both the primary and the dual

inclusion and exclusion formulae can be used. As indicated in Problem 42, these formulae are closely related.

The following examples are applications of the inclusion and exclusion formula in the theory of combinations.

Problem 58   This is the Bernoulli-Euler Problem of inter-changed letters.* A man writes m letters and addresses the corresponding envelopes. In how many ways can he insert the letters into the envelopes without putting any letter into its correct envelope?

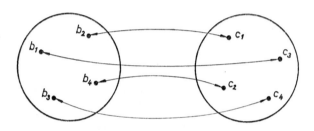

Fig. 38

Every insertion results in a one-to-one correspondence between the set B of letters and the set C of envelopes (Figure 38). A completely correct insertion corresponds to the correspondence

$$b_i \leftrightarrow c_i.$$

If the elements b_i and c_i are identified, a one-to-one mapping of B onto C produces a one-to-one mapping of the set B onto itself, i.e. a permutation. An insertion in which no letter is placed in its correct envelope corresponds to a permutation of the elements of B without a fixed point.** The problem may now be reformulated as follows: how many permutations of m elements are there which leave no point fixed?

*This problem is also attributed to Montmort.
**Such a permutation is often called a *derangement*.

In order to solve this problem, we introduce the following sets:

$U = \{P \mid P \text{ is a permutation of the elements } b_1, b_2, \ldots, b_m\}$,
$A_i = \{P \mid P \in U, P \text{ has the fixed element } b_i\}$.

It follows that $A_i \cap A_j$ is the set of all permutations with the fixed points b_i and b_j.

The number, $\sigma_0 (m)$, of permutations without fixed points is given by the order of the set $(A_1 \cup A_2 \cup \ldots \cup A_m)'$:

$$\sigma_0(m) = n((A_1 \cup A_2 \cup \ldots \cup A_m)')$$
$$= n(U) - \sum_{i=1}^{m} n(A_i) + \sum_{i<j}^{m} n(A_i \cap A_j) - \ldots .$$

It can be seen that:

$$n(A_i) = (m-1)! \text{ for all } i,$$
$$n(A_i \cap A_j) = (m-2)! \text{ for all } i < j,$$
$$n(A_i \cap A_j \cap A_k) = (m-3)! \text{ for all } i < j < k, \text{ etc.}$$

Hence,

$$\sigma_0 (m) = m! - m(m-1)! + \binom{m}{2}(m-2)!$$
$$- \binom{m}{3}(m-3)! + \ldots + (-1)^m \binom{m}{m}(m-m)!$$
$$= m! \left[\frac{1}{2!} - \frac{1}{3!} + \frac{1}{4!} - \ldots + (-1)^m \frac{1}{m!} \right].*$$

Thus

$$\sigma_0(m) = m! \sum_{k=2}^{m} (-1)^k \frac{1}{k!} .$$

It follows, therefore, that for $m = 4$,

$$\sigma_0(4) = 24 \left(\frac{1}{2} - \frac{1}{6} + \frac{1}{24} \right) = 9.$$

*The expression in the square brackets can be rewritten as
$$1 - \frac{1}{1!} + \frac{1}{2!} - \frac{1}{3!} + \ldots ,$$
the first items in the alternating series for e^{-1}. In fact, $m! \, e^{-1}$ is a good approximation to $\sigma_0 (m)$.

If the permuted elements are denoted by a, b, c and d, then the 24 permutations are, in alphabetical order:

abcd	*bacd*	*cabd*	*dabc*
abdc	*badc*	*cadb*	*dacb*
acbd	*bcad*	*cbad*	*dbac*
acdb	*bcda*	*cbda*	*dbca*
adbc	*bdac*	*cdab*	*dcab*
adcb	*bdca*	*cdba*	*dcba*

In a permutation without a fixed point, a must not be in the first position, b not in the second, c not in the third, and d not in the fourth. The nine permutations without fixed points are underlined.

Problem 59   Find the number of permutations of m elements having exactly r fixed points.

This problem is a generalization of the Bernoulli-Euler problem. How many ways are there of inserting the m letters into the m envelopes so that exactly r of the addressees receive the letter intended for them?

Obviously, the solution of this problem is given by Jordan's formula. If we denote the required number by $\sigma_r(m)$, we find that:

$$\sigma_r(m) = \sum_{k=0}^{m-r} (-1)^k \binom{r+k}{k} \Phi_{r+k}^{(m)}(A)$$

with

$$\Phi_{r+k}^{(m)} = \sum_{i_1 < i_2 \ldots < i_{r+k}}^{m} n(A_{i_1} \cap A_{i_2} \cap \ldots \cap A_{i_{r+k}}).$$

However,

$$n(A_{i_1} \cap A_{i_2} \cap \ldots \cap A_{i_{r+k}}) = (m-r-k)!$$

for all $i_1 < i_2 < \ldots < i_{r+k}$, and therefore

$$\Phi_{r+k}^{(m)} = \binom{m}{r+k}(m-r-k)!,$$

and finally

$$\sigma_r(m) = \sum_{k=0}^{m-r} (-1)^k \frac{m!}{k!r!} = \frac{m!}{r!} \sum_{k=0}^{m-r} (-1)^k \frac{1}{k!}.$$

If we apply these results to the case $m = 4$, we obtain:

$$\sigma_1(4) = 24 \sum_{k=0}^{3} (-1)^k \frac{1}{k!} = 24[1-1+\tfrac{1}{2}-\tfrac{1}{6}] = 8,$$

$$\sigma_2(4) = 12 \sum_{k=0}^{2} (-1)^k \frac{1}{k!} = 12[1-1+\tfrac{1}{2}] = 6,$$

$$\sigma_3(4) = \;\; 4 \sum_{k=0}^{1} (-1)^k \frac{1}{k!} = 4[1-1] = 0,$$

$$\sigma_4(4) = \;\; 1.$$

Figure 39 shows the Venn diagram for $n = 4$; the numbers indicate the order of the individual subsets. Since the sets A_i are symmetrically defined, all intersections of exactly r of them have the same order.

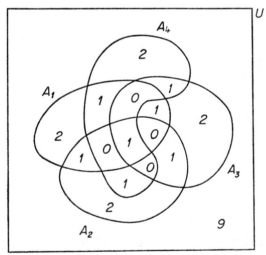

Fig. 39

Problem 60   Euler's function $\varphi(m)$ of a natural number m is the number of elements of the set

$$U = \{1, 2, \ldots, m\}$$

which are relatively prime to m. Find $\varphi(m)$.

Let the factorization of m into primes give

$$m = p_1^{\alpha_1} \cdot p_2^{\alpha_2} \cdot \ldots \cdot p_r^{\alpha_r} \text{ where } p_i \neq p_j \text{ for } i \neq j.$$

In order to obtain $\varphi(m)$, we introduce the following sets:

$$A_i = \{x \mid x \in U, x \text{ divisible by } p_i\} = \{p_i, 2p_i, 3p_i, \ldots, \frac{m}{p_i} p_i\}.$$

We then obtain the orders of the sets A_i and their intersections:

$$n(A_i) = \frac{m}{p_i},$$

$$n(A_i \cap A_j) = \frac{m}{p_i p_j}, i < j,$$

$$n(A_{i_1} \cap A_{i_2} \cap \ldots \cap A_{i_k}) = \frac{m}{p_{i_1} p_{i_2} \cdots p_{i_k}}, i_1 < i_2 < \ldots < i_k.$$

The Venn diagram in Figure 40 illustrates the case $m = 12$.

$$12 = 2^2 \cdot 3,$$
$$A_1 = \{2, 4, 6, 8, 10, 12\},$$
$$A_2 = \{3, 6, 9, 12\},$$
$$A_1 \cap A_2 = \{6, 12\}.$$

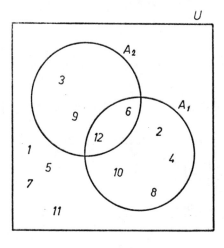

Fig.40

The inclusion and exclusion formula gives:

$$\begin{aligned}
\varphi(m) &= n\big((A_1 \cup A_2 \cup \ldots \cup A_r)'\big) \\
&= n(U) - \sum_{i=1}^{r} n(A_i) + \sum_{i<j}^{r} n(A_i \cap A_j) - \ldots \\
&= m - \sum_{i=1}^{r} \frac{m}{p_i} + \sum_{i<j}^{r} \frac{m}{p_i p_j} - \ldots \\
&= m\left[1 - \sum_{i=1}^{r} \frac{1}{p_i} + \sum_{i<j}^{r} \frac{1}{p_i\, p_j} - \ldots \right] \\
&= m\left(1 - \frac{1}{p_1}\right)\left(1 - \frac{1}{p_2}\right) \ldots \left(1 - \frac{1}{p_r}\right).
\end{aligned}$$

Hence,

$$\varphi(m) = m \prod_{i=1}^{r} \left(1 - \frac{1}{p_i}\right).$$

$\varphi(m)$ may also be obtained by means of the dual inclusion and exclusion formula. Then, the argument goes as follows:

$$\begin{aligned}
\varphi(m) &= n(A_1' \cap A_2' \cap A_3' \cap \ldots \cap A_r') \\
&= \sum_{i=1}^{r} n(A_i') - \sum_{i<j}^{r} n(A_i' \cup A_j') + \ldots.
\end{aligned}$$

However,

$$n(A_i') = m - \frac{m}{p_i} = m\left(1 - \frac{1}{p_i}\right),$$

$$n(A_i' \cup A_j') = n\big((A_i \cap A_j)'\big) = m\left(1 - \frac{1}{p_i\, p_j}\right).$$

$$\begin{aligned}
n(A_1' &\cap A_2' \cap A_3' \cap \ldots \cap A_r') \\
&= m\left[\binom{r}{1} - \binom{r}{2} + \binom{r}{3} - \ldots + (-1)^{r+1}\binom{r}{r} \right] - \sum_{i=1}^{r} \frac{m}{p_i} \\
&\quad + \sum_{i<j}^{r} \frac{m}{p_i\, p_j} - \ldots + (-1)^r \frac{m}{p_1\, p_2 \ldots p_r}.
\end{aligned}$$

Hence,

$$\varphi(m) = m\left(1-\frac{1}{p_1}\right)\left(1-\frac{1}{p_2}\right)\ldots\left(1-\frac{1}{p_r}\right).$$

Problem 61 Show that the following two relations are valid for $a_1, a_2, \ldots, a_\rho \in N$:

$$\max(a_1, a_2, \ldots, a_\rho) = \sum_{j_1=1}^{\rho} a_{j_1} - \sum_{j_1<j_2}^{\rho} \min(a_{j_1}, a_{j_2}) + \ldots$$

$$\ldots + (-1)^\rho \min(a_1, a_2, \ldots, a_\rho);$$

$$\min(a_1, a_2, \ldots, a_\rho) = \sum_{j_1=1}^{\rho} a_{j_1} - \sum_{j_1<j_2}^{\rho} \max(a_{j_1}, a_{j_2}) + \ldots$$

$$\ldots + (-1)^\rho \max(a_1, a_2, \ldots, a_\rho).$$

Further applications of the inclusion and exclusion formula in the theory of combinations can be found in [7], [8], and [11].

3

THE ALGEBRA OF EVENTS

In the calculus of probabilities we are concerned with events, the occurrence of which depends on chance. Before we can deal with this calculus, however, we must discuss in greater detail what we mean by an event. We shall always be concerned with events which are linked with the result of a trial.

3.1 LATTICES OF EVENTS

In order to explain what we understand by an event linked with a trial, we shall consider a simple example of a trial, namely, rolling a die. The outcome of the trial can be characterized by certain features. For an ordinary die, these features are the spots 1 to 6; for a poker die, they are figures taken from playing cards. Every result is described by the feature appearing on the top surface of the die. It will be assumed that the die always come to rest on a face and that we are capable of deciding which surface is uppermost. For example, if poker dice are thrown in the dark, we can no longer describe the result of the trial. If a '2' has been thrown with an ordinary dice, the event of "throwing a '2'" has taken place or occurred. This is characterized by the feature '2 spots'. If another number of spots has been thrown and the same event is under consideration, it will be said that "throwing a '2'" has not occurred.

We shall denote events by means of capital letters. To describe an event, braces, { }, will be used, as in the description of a set, the features characterizing the event being placed within the braces. Thus, the event "throwing a '2'" is written

$$A = \{2 \text{ spots}\}.$$

The non-occurrence of an event A is also an occurrence, called the negation of A and it is denoted by A'.

If an event B occurs whenever A occurs and does not occur when A does not occur, then we say that A and B are equivalent and we write $A = B$. Obviously, this relation is reflexive, symmetric and transitive.

Example 1 A coin is thrown. The events linked with this trial are:

$$H = \{\text{Head}\}, \qquad T = \{\text{Tail}\}.$$

In addition, we could also imagine the event neither head nor tail. This event would occur if a coin came to rest on its edge. In what follows we shall ignore this possible outcome. It follows then that

$$H' = T \quad \text{and} \quad T' = H.$$

Example 2 We shall consider the throw of a die. The following are some possible events:

$$E_i = \{i \text{ spots}\},$$
$$E_e = \{\text{an even number of spots}\},$$
$$E_o = \{\text{an odd number of spots}\}.$$

Once again we shall assume that the die comes to rest with one face clearly uppermost. Then,

$$E_e' = E_o \quad \text{and} \quad E_o' = E_e.$$

Example 3 An urn contains 5 red, 3 green and 4 white balls. The trial consists of drawing a ball from the urn. The events linked with this trial are:

$$E_r = \{\text{the ball drawn is red}\},$$
$$E_g = \{\text{the ball drawn is green}\},$$
$$E_w = \{\text{the ball drawn is white}\}.$$

The trial could be changed by demanding that two balls be drawn from the urn. In this case, amongst the possible events would be:

$$E_1 = \{\text{the balls drawn are both red}\},$$
$$E_2 = \{\text{one ball is red, the other green}\},$$
$$E_3 = \{\text{neither of the balls is white}\}.$$

With every trial, there must be some means of determining whether or not a particular event has occurred. Thus, a colour-blind person carrying out this trial, would not be capable of deciding whether the events E_1 and E_2 have occurred or not.

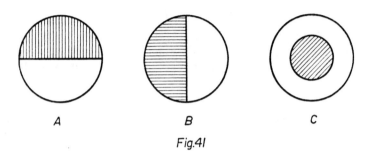

A   B   C

Fig.41

Example 4 A marksman shoots at a circular target. Every shot is regarded as one trial. Possible events include, for example (see Figure 41):

$A = \{$hit in the upper half of the target$\}$,

$B = \{$hit in the left-hand half of the target$\}$,

$C = \{$hit within a circle with radius half that of the target and with the same centre$\}$.

Every marksman knows that with such definitions of the events A, B and C, it would, in many cases, be impossible to decide whether or not an event had occurred. This would be the case when the shot hits a boundary line. Thus, C would have to be defined more precisely, for example, by saying that it also occurs if the defining circle is cut. The definition of the events A and B can also be stated more accurately, and when this example is mentioned again we shall assume that this has been done.

After these simple examples, we shall deal with combinations of several events.

Definition 1 $A \cup B$ is the event that at least one of the events A, B occurs; i.e.,

$$A \cup B = \{A \text{ or } B\}.$$

It follows directly from this definition of $A \cup B$ that

$$A \cup B = B \cup A. \tag{Ia}$$

We shall illustrate this compounding operation by reference to the preceding examples, and shall use the letters introduced for the individual events.

From Example 1:

$$H \cup T.$$

This event means 'after the throw, either a head or a tail appears'. In view of the restriction we made for this trial, the occurrence of this event is certain. An event which is bound to occur will be denoted by U and will be referred to as the *certain event*. Consequently,

$$U = H \cup T.$$

From Example 2:

$$(E_2 \cup E_4) \cup E_6.$$

This event means an even number is thrown. We can write

$$E_e = (E_2 \cup E_4) \cup E_6.$$

We also have

$$U = E_e \cup E_o.$$

Definition 2 $A \cap B$ is the event that A and B both occur; i.e.,

$$A \cap B = \{A \text{ and } B\}.$$

Again, it follows from the definition that

$$A \cap B = B \cap A. \tag{Ib}$$

In Example 4 the compound event $A \cap B$ means 'a hit in the left upper quarter of the target'. This example shows clearly that $A \cap B$ is linked with the intersection of two point sets.

From Example 1:

$H \cap T =$ head and tail facing upwards simultaneously.

This event cannot occur; such an event is called an *impossible event* and is denoted by $\emptyset$. Hence, in this example

$$H \cap T = \emptyset.$$

An impossible event would also be to throw 7 spots with one die, or simultaneously 2 and 3 spots. Hence we can write

$$E_7 = \emptyset \quad \text{and} \quad E_2 \cap E_3 = \emptyset.$$

The distributive law

$$A \cup (B \cap C) = (A \cup B) \cap (A \cup C) \tag{IIa}$$

can be easily verified. The event $A \cup (B \cap C)$ occurs when A and/or $B \cap C$ occur. However, when A occurs, the events $A \cup B$ and $A \cup C$ also both occur. Again both $A \cup B$ and $A \cup C$ occur when B and C occur simultaneously. This shows that $(A \cup B) \cap (A \cup C)$ occurs whenever $A \cup (B \cap C)$ occurs, and it is easy to show that the converse holds, which completes the proof of IIa. In the same way it is also possible to verify the distributive law

$$A \cap (B \cup C) = (A \cap B) \cup (A \cap C). \tag{IIb}$$

$A \cap (B \cup C)$ occurs when A and either B or C occurs. These are the same conditions that govern the occurrence of either $A \cap B$ or $A \cap C$, i.e., of $(A \cap B) \cup (A \cap C)$.

It can also easily be confirmed that the certain event U and the impossible event $\emptyset$ satisfy the following laws:

$$\left. \begin{array}{ll} A \cup \emptyset \ = \emptyset \cup A = A & \text{(IIIa)} \\ A \cap U \ = U \cap A = A & \text{(IIIb)} \\ A \cup A' = U & \text{(IVa)} \\ A \cap A' = \emptyset & \text{(IVb)} \end{array} \right\} \text{ for all } A.$$

Thus, all the axioms of a Boolean lattice have been verified. Hence:

Theorem The set of events associated with a given trial (including the certain event and the impossible event) is a

Boolean lattice relative to the two compounding operations ∪ and ∩ and the operation of negation.*

It follows from the theorem that all the rules and Theorems of a Boolean lattice apply to our set of events. We call it the lattice of events associated with a given trial.

We end this section with a simple example, in which the compound events are also formulated linguistically.

Example 5   Two cards are drawn simultaneously from a pack of cards. The following events will be considered first:

$$R = \{\text{two red cards}\},$$
$$Q = \{\text{two queens}\}.$$

In the associated algebra of events, the following combinations occur:

$$R \cup Q = \{\text{two red cards or two queens}\},$$
$$R \cap Q = \{\text{two red queens}\},$$
$$R' \cap Q = \{\text{two black queens}\},$$
$$(R \cap Q') \cup (R' \cap Q) = \{\text{two red cards which are not}$$
$$\text{queens, or two black queens}\}.$$

It was mentioned in Section 2.2 that a partial order may be constructed on a Boolean lattice by the equivalence

$$A \subset B \Leftrightarrow A \cap B = A.$$

We shall now demonstrate the importance of this partial ordering on a lattice of events. In order to do this, we shall look again at Example 2. There, it is obviously true that $E_2 \cap E_e = E_2$ or $E_2 \subset E_e$. $E_2 \cap E_e$ is the same event as E_2, i.e., every time E_2 occurs, E_e also takes place. $E_2 \subset E_e$ expresses that E_2 is always associated with E_e.

Generally, $A = A \cap B$ is equivalent to saying that the occurrence of B always follows upon the occurrence of A, i.e., A brings about B.

---

*For the zero element of this lattice we have chosen the same sign Ø as for that of the power set lattice.

In any Boolean lattice

$$A = A \cap B \Leftrightarrow B = A \cup B.$$

(See Section 1.3.4; what was demonstrated there for a power set lattice holds for every Boolean lattice.)

We can further conclude from the first distributive law that

$$A \cup (A' \cap B) = (A \cup A') \cap (A \cup B) = U \cap (A \cup B) = A \cup B,$$

so the following equivalences hold in general:

$$A \subset B \Leftrightarrow A \cap B = A \Leftrightarrow A \cup B = B \Leftrightarrow A \cup (A' \cap B) = B.$$
$$\text{(1)} \qquad\qquad\qquad \text{(2)}$$

3.2 THE STRUCTURE OF FINITE LATTICES OF EVENTS

In the following, we shall limit ourselves to trials for which the number of possible events is finite. This type of trial includes Examples 1, 2, 3 and 5.

The elements of a finite lattice of events may be separated into different classes.

Definition An element A of the lattice L of events is said to be an *elementary* event if it satisfies the following two conditions:

(a) $A \neq \varnothing$,
(b) $A \cap B = \varnothing$ or A, for every $B \in L$.

We shall show that the events $E_1, E_2, \ldots, E_6$ in Example 2 are elementary. Clearly they differ from $\varnothing$, and

$$E_j \cap E_k = \begin{cases} \varnothing \text{ for } j \neq k, \\ E_j \text{ for } j = k. \end{cases}$$

It remains to be shown that (b) is satisfied for $A = E_i$ and for $B \in L$. Generally, an event can arise only by combinations of E_i and E_j, because the terms $E_1, E_2, \ldots, E_6$ completely describe all possible results of the trial. If, in a representation of B, there occurs, for example, E_1', then this can be replaced by $E_2 \cup E_3 \cup \ldots \cup E_6$. A term such as $E_1 \cap E_2$ can always be replaced by $\varnothing$, as can a term such as $E_j \cap \varnothing$. In a term of the form $E_j \cup \varnothing$, $\varnothing$ can simply be omitted. Thus, any event is either $\varnothing$ or can be represented in the form

$$B = E_{j_1} \cup E_{j_2} \cup \ldots \cup E_{j_s}.$$

If $B = \varnothing$, $E_i \cap B = \varnothing$, and (b) has been proved. If B has the form given above, we use the distributive law:

$$E_i \cap (E_{j_1} \cup E_{j_2} \cup \ldots \cup E_{j_s})$$
$$= (E_i \cap E_{j_1}) \cup (E_i \cap E_{j_2}) \cup \ldots \cup (E_i \cap E_{j_s}).$$

However, this term is equal to E_i or $\varnothing$, according to whether E_i occurs in the representation of B or not. Thus, property (b) has been fully proved.

Definition An event is a *compound* event if it can be represented in the form

$$A = B \cup C \quad \text{with} \quad B \neq A \quad \text{and} \quad C \neq A.$$

The condition $B \neq A$ and $C \neq A$ excludes the trivial representations

$$A = A \cup \varnothing \quad \text{and} \quad A = A \cup A$$

which hold for every event.

Theorem 1 An elementary event cannot be compound.

Proof Let us assume that the elementary event A is compound. Then it can be represented in the form

$$A = B \cup C \quad \text{with} \quad B \neq A \quad \text{and} \quad C \neq A.$$

It follows, therefore, that

$$A \cap B = (B \cup C) \cap B = B \cap (B \cup C)$$
$$= (B \cap B) \cup (B \cap C) = B \cup (B \cap C) = B \neq A$$

which contradicts condition (b) of the definition of an elementary event since $B \neq \varnothing$ ($B = \varnothing$ implies $C = A$ which again leads to a contradiction).

In addition, we have

Theorem 2   A non-elementary event $A \neq \varnothing$ is necessarily compound.

Proof   If A is non-elementary and $A \neq \varnothing$, there exists, since condition (b) does not hold, an element $B \neq \varnothing$ such that

$$A \cap B \neq \varnothing \quad \text{and} \quad A \cap B \neq A.$$

We recall the two equivalences

$$A \cap B = \varnothing \Leftrightarrow A \cap B' = A,$$

and

$$A \cap B = A \Leftrightarrow A \cap B' = \varnothing,$$

and note that they can also be expressed in the form

$$A \cap B \neq \varnothing \Leftrightarrow A \cap B' \neq A,$$

and

$$A \cap B \neq A \Leftrightarrow A \cap B' \neq \varnothing.$$

Our event A can be represented as

$$A = A \cap (B \cup B') = (A \cap B) \cup (A \cap B'),$$

and, with the aid of the equivalences given above, we see that

$$A \cap B \neq \begin{cases} A \\ \varnothing \end{cases} \quad \text{and} \quad A \cap B' \neq \begin{cases} A \\ \varnothing. \end{cases}$$

We have, therefore, represented A in a way which shows that this element is compound.

The impossible event $\varnothing$ plays a special role in this classification of events. We note, moreover, that the event $\varnothing$ is neither elementary nor compound. It is not elementary, in view of the condition (a) in the definition of an elementary event. It cannot be compound, since it cannot be represented in the form

$$\varnothing = A \cup B \quad \text{with} \quad A \neq \varnothing.$$

The following theorem is a further characterization of an elementary event.

Theorem 3   The event $A \neq \varnothing$ is elementary if, and only if, there is no B differing from $\emptyset$ and A for which $B \subset A$; i.e., if there is no possible event B which differs from A and the occurrence of which would bring about the occurrence of A.

Proof (a) Let us assume first that there is a B differing from $\emptyset$ and A for which $B \subset A$. We have to show that A cannot be elementary.

It was shown at the end of Section 3.1 that $B \subset A$ is equivalent to the two relations:

$$B = A \cap B, \tag{1}$$

and

$$A = B \cup (A \cap B'). \tag{2}$$

In order to demonstrate the compound nature of A, it is sufficient to show that in (2) $A \cap B' \neq A$, since, by assumption, $B \neq \emptyset$ and $B \neq A$. If it were true that $A \cap B' = A$, then it would follow from (1) that

$$B = (A \cap B') \cap B = A \cap (B \cap B') = A \cap \emptyset = \emptyset,$$

which would contradict the assumption that $B \neq \emptyset$.

(b) A will now be assumed to be non-elementary; i.e., there exist B and C such that $A = B \cup C$ with $B \neq A$ and $C \neq A$.

(Again $B \neq \emptyset$, since this would imply $C = A$.) We have therefore found a B such that $B \neq \emptyset$, $B \neq A$ and $B \subset A$, and this completes the proof of the theorem.

The relevance of elementary events is expressed in the following theorem.

Theorem 4 Every compound event A of a finite lattice of events can be uniquely represented as the union of a set of elementary events.

In order to prove this theorem we shall first establish two lemmas.

Lemma 1 The intersection $E_1 \cap E_2$ of two elementary events $E_1 \neq E_2$ is always equal to $\emptyset$.

Proof If follows from the condition (b) of the definition of an elementary event that

$$E_1 \cap E_2 = \emptyset \text{ or } E_1,$$
$$E_2 \cap E_1 = \emptyset \text{ or } E_2.$$

Since $E_1 \neq E_2$ and $E_1 \cap E_2 = E_2 \cap E_1$, the only remaining possibility is $E_1 \cap E_2 = \emptyset$.

Lemma 2 Given any compound event A we can find an elementary event E satisfying the relation $E \subset A$.

Proof Since A is compound, then by Theorem 3, there exists an event B_1 such that $B_1 \neq \emptyset$, $B_1 \neq A$ and $B_1 \subset A$. If B_1 is an elementary event then the proof is completed. If not, then, by Theorem 2, B_1 is a compound event, and there exists by Theorem 3, an event B_2 with the properties $B_2 \neq \emptyset$, $B_2 \neq B_1$ and $B_2 \subset B_1$. In a finite lattice of events, this process must terminate after a finite number of steps. Finally, an event B_n is found such that $B_n \neq \emptyset$, $B_n \neq B_{n-1}$, $B_n \subset B_{n-1}$ and B_n is elementary. We denote this elementary event B_n by E_1. Since the relation $\subset$ is transitive, this elementary event E_1 satisfies the relation $E_1 \subset A$.

Proof of Theorem 4 If A is compound, there exists, by Lemma 2, an elementary event E_1 satisfying the relation $E_1 \subset A$. For the pair of events, A and E_1 we can write, as in the proof of Theorem 2,

$$A = (A \cap E_1) \cup (A \cap E_1').$$

However, from the relation $E_1 \subset A$ it follows that

$$E_1 = A \cap E_1,$$

and so

$$A = E_1 \cup (A \cap E_1') = E_1 \cup A_1, \text{ say.}$$

If A_1 is not an elementary event, then we can repeat this process. Since the lattice is finite, the method must terminate after a finite number of steps. The compound event A can, therefore, always be represented in the form

$$A = E_1 \cup E_2 \cup E_3 \cup \ldots \cup E_r.$$

Such a presentation is called a *canonical representation*. In order to complete the proof of Theorem 4, it must be proved that the canonical representation is unique apart from possible changes in the order in which the elementary events are written.

Let us assume that there exist two canonical representations of A:

$$A = E_1 \cup E_2 \cup \ldots \cup E_r \quad \text{and} \quad A = E_1^* \cup E_2^* \cup \ldots \cup E_s^*.$$

Then

$$E_1 \cup E_2 \cup \ldots \cup E_r = E_1^* \cup E_2^* \cup \ldots \cup E_s^*.$$

Since these two representations differ, at least one event occurs in one but not in the other. Without loss of generality we can suppose that E_1 does not occur in the second representation; i.e.

$$E_1 \neq E_i^* \ (i = 1, 2, \ldots, s).$$

We now form $E_1 \cap A$. Using Lemma 1, we obtain from the first representation:

$$E_1 \cap A = E_1,$$

and from the second:

$$E_1 \cap A = \emptyset,$$

which is a contradiction, since E_1 is elementary. Thus, two canonical representations of A can differ only in the order in which the elementary events occurring are written, and this is irrelevant in view of the commutative law.

Theorem 5 The number of events in a finite lattice of events is a power of 2.

Proof Let the lattice of events contain n elementary events:

$$E_1, E_2, \ldots, E_n.$$

Every event A of the lattice may, according to Theorem 4, be represented uniquely as the union of a set of elementary events. With regard to A, there are two possibilities for every E_i: either it occurs in the canonical representation of A or it does not. The number of elements in this lattice is therefore 2^n (cf Problems 22 and 30).

In the literature, the term *algebra of events* is sometimes used instead of lattice of events.

We shall now enumerate all the events in an example of a finite lattice of events.

Example 6   The trial consists of the throwing of two coins.

The associated algebra of events contains four elementary events, namely:

$$E_1 = \{\text{head, head}\},$$
$$E_2 = \{\text{head, tail}\},$$
$$E_3 = \{\text{tail, head}\},$$
$$E_4 = \{\text{tail, tail}\}.$$

Altogether, there are $2^4 = 16$ events which can easily be enumerated:

φ;

E_1, E_2, E_3, E_4;

$E_i \cup E_j$ for $i < j$ (6 events of this kind);

E_1', E_2', E_3', E_4';

$E_1 \cup E_2 \cup E_3 \cup E_4 = U.$

3.3   EVENT SPACES

Theorem 4 reveals the structure of the algebra of a finite lattice of events. We shall now demonstrate this by means of a simple model. In order to do this we shall consider the set Γ of elementary events forming part of a given trial:

$$\Gamma = \{E_1, E_2, \ldots, E_n\}.$$

Γ is called the *event space* belonging to this test.* To illustrate the event space we may use an equivalent point set in the plane of the drawing. According to Theorem 4, every event A may be mapped onto a subset R of the event space, the subset consisting of those points which are associated with the elementary events occurring in the canonical representation

---

*The terms *sampling space* and *possibility space* are also used.

of A. Naturally, the certain event is mapped onto the set Γ and the impossible event onto the empty set. It is easy to see that the following mappings also apply:

$$X \cup Y \leftrightarrow R_x \mathbin{\underset{\sim}{\cup}} R_y,$$
$$X \cap Y \leftrightarrow R_x \mathbin{\underset{\sim}{\cap}} R_y,$$
$$X' \leftrightarrow R'_x,$$

where the unions, intersections and complements are on the power set $P(\Gamma)$. In order to distinguish these operations from those in the lattice of events, they are denoted in Chapters 3 and 4 by $\underset{\sim}{\cup}$ and $\underset{\sim}{\cap}$.

Using the event space, we can illustrate Examples 2 and 6 by means of Venn diagrams.

The event space for Example 2 consists of six elements. The lines surrounding the points representing the elements E_i represent the events E_e and E_o. (Figure 42).

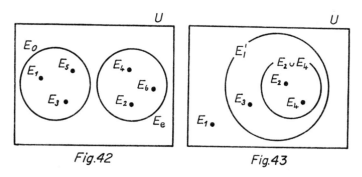

Fig.42   Fig.43

Example 6 refers to an event space with four elements. Figure 43 shows the subsets corresponding to the events E'_1 and $E_2 \cup E_4$.

An important extension of the event space arises if two different trials are combined to form a new one. For example, if rolling a die is combined with tossing a coin, the new event space may be described in terms of the event spaces of the two constituent trials. Let Γ_1 be the event space for rolling the die and Γ_2 the event space for tossing the coin. An elementary event of the combined trial always springs from elementary events of the constituent trials. The elementary events of the combined trial are, in fact, associated with ordered pairs of the constituent elementary events. There are altogether $6 \times 2 = 12$ such pairs, and these are listed in the following table.

Γ_1

		E_1	E_2	E_3	E_4	E_5	E_6
Γ_2	H	HE_1	HE_2	HE_3	HE_4	HE_5	HE_6
	T	TE_1	TE_2	TE_3	TE_4	TE_5	TE_6

Fig 44

The event space of the combined trial is the Cartesian product $\Gamma_1 \times \Gamma_2$ of the two event spaces Γ_1 and Γ_2. For the trial consisting of throwing two dice, the elementary events would be given by ordered pairs of events formed from two identical spaces (Γ_1). The corresponding event space is the product $\Gamma_1 \times \Gamma_1$.

In the next chapter we shall see how the correspondence between the lattice of events and the power set lattice can prepare the way for Kolmogorov's approach to the theory of probability.

3.4 FINITE BOOLEAN LATTICES

The reasoning in Section 3.2 can be applied without any change to every finite Boolean lattice. In Section 3.2, finite lattices of events were considered more or less in place of the more general finite Boolean lattices.

In a general Boolean lattice the elements corresponding to the elementary events are called *atomic* elements or *atoms*.

According to Section 3.2, a Boolean lattice with n atomic elements has altogether 2^n elements; moreover, if U is a set of order n, then the power set lattice $[P(U), \cup, \cap]$ has the same number of elements. This state of affairs appears to indicate that every finite Boolean lattice may be made to correspond to a power set lattice. In fact, the following relationship holds:

Theorem 6 Every finite Boolean lattice is isomorphic to a power set lattice.

In view of this, the structure of the power set lattices will be present in other Boolean lattices.

Proof Let us consider the finite lattice $[L, \cup, \cap]$ with the zero element O, the unit element E, and with

$$\Gamma = \{A_1, A_2, \ldots, A_n\}$$

as the set of its atomic elements. The results of Section 3.2 tell us that L may be described as follows:

$$L = \{X \mid \underbrace{X = (S_1 \cap A_1) \cup (S_2 \cap A_2) \cup \ldots \cup (S_n \cap A_n)}_{\text{canonical representation of } X};$$
$$S_j = O \text{ or } E\}.$$

In addition, we shall also consider the power set of Γ,

$$P(\Gamma) = \{R_x \mid R_x \subset \Gamma\},$$

i.e., the set of all subsets R_x of Γ.

The correspondence

$$X = A_{j_1} \cup A_{j_2} \cup \ldots \cup A_{j_r} \leftrightarrow R_x = \{A_{j_1}, A_{j_2}, \ldots, A_{j_r}\}$$

between the elements of L and $P(\Gamma)$ is obviously a one-to-one relation.

It is also true that for the mapping

$$X \overset{\omega}{\to} R_x,$$

we have

$$\omega(X \cup Y) = R_x \underset{\sim}{\cup} R_y,$$
$$\omega(X \cap Y) = R_x \underset{\sim}{\cap} R_y,$$
$$\omega(X') = R'_x.$$

The mapping ω is, therefore, an isomorphism, and the two lattices $[L, \cup, \cap]$ and $[P(\Gamma), \underset{\sim}{\cup}, \underset{\sim}{\cap}]$ are isomorphic.

The American mathematician M. H. Stone showed in 1936

that *every* Boolean lattice is isomorphic to some family of subsets of a set.* The proof of this theorem of Boolean algebra, however, goes beyond the range of this book.

Example 4 of Section 3.3 can be used to illustrate this general representation theorem. Shooting at a target implies a continuous and therefore infinite space of events. Obviously, every event X can be mapped onto a set of points R_x on the target. The set of all possible R_x is the power set of the set S forming the target. The isomorphism between the lattice of events and a power set lattice appears clearly in this example.

Problem 62   Which are the atomic elements of the power set lattice generated by $U = \{a, b, c, d\}$ and where do they appear in the Hasse diagram?

Problem 63   Which are the atomic elements in the lattice in Problem 36, and where do they appear in the Hasse diagram?

Problem 64   Every definition or theorem in a lattice $[L, \cup, \cap]$ which is not symmetrical with respect to the operations $\cup$ and $\cap$ or to the elements O and E, can be dualized.

   (a) Dualize the concept of *atomic element* in a finite Boolean lattice. Find the dual elements to the atoms in the lattices of Problems 62 and 36 and locate them in the corresponding Hasse diagrams.
   (b) Dualize the *canonical representation* of the elements of a finite Boolean lattice.

*Note that it is not true that an infinite Boolean lattice is necessarily isomorphic to the set of *all* subsets of a set; indeed infinite Boolean lattices exist with a countable number of elements, whereas the power set of an infinite set is never countable. The proof of Stone's Theorem is given in [12].

4

AN INTRODUCTION
TO PROBABILITY

4.1 RELATIVE FREQUENCY

We shall endeavour to explain the concept of probability by means of relative frequency. This will be introduced by an example already considered.

Problem 65 Three players, Alfred, Bruno and Caesar, each in turn draw one card from a pack. A drawn card is immediately returned to the pack before the next player draws his card. Such a triple draw (one per player) is regarded as a trial.

Consider the following events:

$$A = \{\text{Alfred draws a red card}\},$$
$$B = \{\text{Bruno draws a red card}\},$$
$$C = \{\text{Caesar draws a red card}\}.$$

The trial is repeated 50 times. We shall now consider in this series of trials subsets which are associated with the events A, B and C, namely:

$$M_A = \{\text{trials in which Alfred draws a red card}\},$$
$$M_B = \{\text{trials in which Bruno draws a red card}\},$$
$$M_C = \{\text{trials in which Caesar draws a red card}\}.$$

We also introduce:

$$M_U = \{50 \text{ completed trials}\},$$

i.e., M_U is the set we associate with the certain event.

If we complete the data of Problem 12 by supplying the values:

$$\xi = n(M_A \cap M_B \cap M_C) = 7,$$
$$\eta = n(M'_A \cap M'_B \cap M'_C) = 4,$$

we obtain the following orders:

$$n(M_A) = 35, \qquad n(M_B) = 25, \qquad n(M_C) = 28,$$
$$n(M_A \cap M_B) = 15, \qquad n(M_A \cap M_C) = 21, \qquad n(M_B \cap M_C) = 13.$$

The correspondence defined between events and sets extends to give:

$$A \cup B \leftrightarrow M_A \cup M_B,$$
$$A \cap B \leftrightarrow M_A \cap M_B,$$
$$A' \leftrightarrow M_A'.$$

The left-hand column contains the operations in the lattice of events for the trial under review, and the right-hand column those in the power set $P(M_U)$. Thus, for example, A' is the negation of the event A, while M_A' indicates the complement of M_A relative to M_U.

In the power set, n is an additive set function, and so, therefore, is $n/50$. This latter set function is used to define the relative frequency.

Let E be a random element of our algebra of events. We associate this event with the number

$$\frac{n(M_E)}{50} = \frac{n(M_E)}{n(M_U)},$$

in which M_E is that subset of M_U which consists of the trials in our sequence in which the event E occurred. This number associated with E is the *relative frequency* of E in the trial series and is denoted by $f(E)$. Hence by definition,

$$f(E) = \frac{n(M_E)}{n(M_U)}.$$

For example, the events

$$R = A \cap B \cap C = \{\text{all players draw red cards}\},$$

and

$$S = A' \cap B' \cap C' = \{\text{all players draw black cards}\},$$

have the relative frequencies

$$f(R) = \frac{n(M_A \cap M_B \cap M_C)}{n(M_U)} = \frac{7}{50},$$

and

$$f(S) = \frac{n(M'_A \cap M'_B \cap M'_C)}{n(M_U)} = \frac{4}{50}.$$

4.2 RULES FOR CALCULATING THE RELATIVE FREQUENCY

Rules for calculating the relative frequency can be easily established, because we have defined f as an additive set function over the power set of M_U. We find:

I. For every event E,

$$0 \leqslant f(E) \leqslant 1.$$

In particular, $f(U) = 1$ and $f(\emptyset) = 0$.

IIa. If $R \cap S = \emptyset$, then

$$f(R \cup S) = f(R) + f(S).$$

This law is obvious, since it follows from $R \cap S = \emptyset$ that $M_R \cap M_S = M_\phi$ and therefore that

$$n(M_R \cup M_S) = n(M_R) + n(M_S).$$

Hence,

$$f(R \cup S) = \frac{n(M_R \cup M_S)}{n(M_U)} = \frac{n(M_R) + n(M_S)}{n(M_U)}$$
$$= \frac{n(M_R)}{n(M_U)} + \frac{n(M_S)}{n(M_U)} = f(R) + f(S).$$

In our example, $f(R \cup S)$ would be the relative frequency of the event

$R \cup S = \{$all players draw cards of the same colour$\}$.

IIb. In general

$$f(A \cup B) = f(A) + f(B) - f(A \cap B).$$

This property is proved in the same way as IIa, using the relation

$$n(M_A \cup M_B) = n(M_A) + n(M_B) - n(M_A \cap M_B).$$

In our example, the events A and B illustrate this general case.

4.3   THE CONDITIONAL RELATIVE FREQUENCY

If the event A has occurred exactly m times in a series of N trials and in these m trials the event B has occurred k times together with A, the quotient k/m is called the *conditional relative frequency of the event B given A*, and is written $f_A(B)$.

We have,

$$k = n(M_A \cap M_B) \quad \text{and} \quad m = n(M_A),$$

that is,

$$f_A(B) = \frac{n(M_A \cap M_B)}{n(M_A)} = \frac{n(M_A \cap M_B)/n(M_U)}{n(M_A)/n(M_U)}$$
$$= \frac{f(A \cap B)}{(A)}.$$

In our example, we obtain:

$$f_A(B) = \frac{f(A \cap B)}{f(A)} = \frac{15/50}{35/50} = \frac{3}{7}.$$

This is the conditional relative frequency for Bruno drawing a red card given that Alfred also draws a red card.

Obviously, $f_A(B)$ is defined only if $f(A) \neq 0$.

The justification of the concept of relative frequency for $f_A(B)$ can be seen by considering the ordinary relative frequency in a new series of trials, namely in that series which contains only those trials in which event A has occurred. Apart from that, the reader will be able to verify easily that properties I, IIa and IIb of Section 4.2 hold for $f_A(E)$, with the obvious assumption that $f(A) \neq 0$.

4.4 THE CONCEPT OF PROBABILITY

Naturally, the frequency defined for an event depends on the series of trials, i.e., it is a measure which fluctuates according to the results of the trials. Thus, series of equal length can give very different relative frequencies for one and the same event. The reader is recommended to carry out a long series of trials with, for example, a coin or a die and to graph the relative frequency of a particular event as a function of the length of the series. Generally, as the number of trials increases, the relative frequency begins to exhibit a certain stability. Such experiments suggest that one might associate a number with the event, for which the relative frequencies found give approximate values. According to Kolmogorov, this number is called the *probability* of the event. Only observation of the relative frequency can decide whether such a number can be associated with a certain event. In the following, we shall deal only with events for which such a possibility does, in fact, exist. Thus, a sharp distinction must be drawn between probability and relative frequency. Whilst the former is a fixed number associated with the event, depending only on the event and on the trial, the second depends on chance.

4.5 KOLMOGOROV'S PROBABILITY ALGEBRA

4.5.1 *The probability axioms and some propositions*

In accordance with what has been said about the existence of probability, and by analogy with the properties of relative frequency, we postulate the following axioms:

I   With every element E of a lattice of events is associated a non-negative number $p(E)$, the probability of E.

II   The probability of a certain event is always equal to one; i.e., $p(U) = 1$.

III $p(E \cup F) = p(E) + p(F)$ if $E \cap F = \emptyset$.

A lattice of events which satisfies the axioms I, II and III is called a *probability algebra*. The foundations of the probability calculus were laid by A. N. Kolmogorov.

Several important properties of probability can be derived directly from the axioms:

(a) Suppose $B \subset A$, i.e., every time the event B occurs then the event A occurs as well. Then, according to Section 3.1, the following equivalence holds:

$$B \subset A \Leftrightarrow A = A \cup (A \cap B')$$

and

$$B \cap (A \cap B') = \emptyset.$$

Hence, from III it follows that

$$p(A) = p(B) + p(A \cap B').$$

However, according to axiom I, $p(A \cap B')$ is a non-negative number, and so

$$B \subset A \Rightarrow p(B) \leqslant p(A).$$

(b) For every element A,

$$A \cup A' = U \quad \text{and} \quad A \cap A' = \emptyset.$$

However, according to axioms II and III,

$$p(U) = p(A \cup A') = p(A) + p(A') = 1,$$

i.e., *the sum of the probabilities of an event and its negation is equal to* 1. In particular, since $\emptyset = U'$, we have

$$p(\emptyset) = 0,$$

that is, *the impossible event has the probability* 0.

The probability $p(E)$ is, by virtue of axioms I and III, an additive function over the corresponding lattice of events (see Section 2.3). We can state:

(a) If $A_1, A_2, \ldots, A_n$ are events which are mutually exclusive in pairs, i.e.,

$$A_i \cap A_j = \emptyset \quad \text{for} \quad i \neq j,$$

then

$$p(A_1 \cup A_2 \cup \ldots \cup A_n) = p(A_1) + p(A_2) + \ldots + p(A_n).$$

(b) However, more generally we have the inclusion and exclusion formula:

$$p(A_1 \cup A_2 \cup \ldots \cup A_n = \sum_{i=1}^{n} p(A_i) - \sum_{i<j}^{n} p(A_i \cap A_j) + \ldots .$$

4.5.2 Conditional probability

By analogy with conditional relative frequency, we also introduce conditional probability.

Definition By the *conditional probability of the event B given the event A*, we mean the number

$$p_A(B) = \frac{p(A \cap B)}{p(A)} .*$$

This is the probability of the occurrence of B given that the event A has already occurred. Naturally $p_A(B)$ is defined only for $p(A) \neq 0$.

Since $A \cap B \subset A$, it follows from property (a) that

$$p(A \cap B) \leqslant p(A), \quad \text{i.e.,} \quad p_A(B) \leqslant 1.$$

$p(A \cap B)$ and $p(A)$ are both non-negative, therefore,

$$0 \leqslant p_A(B) \leqslant 1.$$

Furthermore, since, if $B \cap C = \emptyset$,

$$(A \cap B) \cap (A \cap C) = A \cap (B \cap C) = A \cap \emptyset = \emptyset,$$

it follows that

$$p_A(B \cup C) = \frac{p[A \cap (B \cup C)]}{p(A)} = \frac{p[(A \cap B) \cup (A \cap C)]}{p(A)}$$
$$= \frac{p(A \cap B) + p(A \cap C)}{p(A)}$$

i.e.

$$p_A(B \cup C) = p_A(B) + p_A(C).$$

*An alternative notation for $p_A(B)$ is $p(B|A)$.

Conditional probabilities therefore satisfy axioms I and III. This further justifies the definition of probability.

It follows from $A \cap B = B \cap A$ and from the definition of conditional probability, assuming of course that $p(A) \neq 0$, $p(B) \neq 0$, that

$$p(A \cap B) = p(A) \cdot p_A(B) = p(B) \cdot p_B(A). \tag{1}$$

In addition,

$$p_U(A) = \frac{p(U \cap A)}{p(U)} = \frac{p(A)}{1} = p(A).$$

Relation (1) may therefore be rewritten as

$$p_U(A) \cdot p_A(B) = p_U(B) \cdot p_B(A). \tag{2}$$

In general, $p_A(B) \neq p_U(B) = p(B)$. However, if $p_A(B) = p(B)$, it follows from (2) that simultaneously

$$p_B(A) = p(A).$$

Definition Two events A and B are said to be mutually *independent* if $p(A) \cdot p(B) \neq 0$ and $p_A(B) = p(B)$.*

It follows from (1) that if A and B are mutually independent events, then

$$p(A \cap B) = p(A) \cdot p(B).$$

If, conversely, $p(A \cap B) = p(A) \cdot p(B)$, and $p(A) \cdot p(B) \neq 0$, the events A and B are independent, for from this assumption it follows that

$$p(A) = \frac{p(A \cap B)}{p(B)} = p_B(A),$$

i.e., the events A and B are independent. Hence we have the following theorem.

*It will, of course, also follow that $p_B(A) = p(A)$.

Theorem Two events A and B for which $p(A) \cdot p(B) \neq 0$ are independent if, and only if,

$$p(A \cap B) = p(A) \cdot p(B).$$

If A and B are random events for which $p(A) \cdot p(B) \neq 0$ then

$$p(A) \cdot p_A(B) = p(B) \cdot p_B(A),$$

that is,

$$\frac{p_A(B)}{p(B)} = \frac{p_B(A)}{p(A)} = \frac{p(A \cap B)}{p(A) \cdot p(B)} = k(A,B), \text{ say.}$$

The function $k(A,B)$, which is symmetrical with respect to A and B, is the *effect coefficient* of the pair of events A,B. If A and B are independent, $k(A,B) = 1$.

We shall now prove the following theorem.

Theorem If A and B are independent events, then it follows that A' and B, A and B', and A' and B' are also mutually independent.

Proof It is sufficient to prove that A and B', and A' and B' are independent.

(a) A and B' are independent.
It is always true that

$$A = (A \cap B') \cup (A \cap B) \quad \text{and} \quad (A \cap B') \cap (A \cap B) = \emptyset.$$

Hence,

$$p(A) = p(A \cap B') + p(A \cap B) = p(A \cap B') + p(A) \cdot p(B).$$

or

$$p(A \cap B') = p(A) - p(A) \cdot p(B) = p(A)[1 - p(B)] = p(A) \cdot p(B').$$

(b) A' and B' are independent.

$$\begin{aligned}
p(A' \cap B') &= p((A \cup B)') = 1 - p(A \cup B) \\
&= 1 - p(A) - p(B) + p(A \cap B) \\
&= 1 - p(A) - p(B) + p(A) \cdot p(B) \\
&= [1 - p(A)][1 - p(B)] \\
&= p(A') \cdot p(B').
\end{aligned}$$

4.6 FINITE PROBABILITY ALGEBRAS AND THE CLASSICAL THEORY OF PROBABILITY

A probability algebra in which only a finite number of events occur is referred to as a *finite probability algebra*. We have found in Section 3.3 that in this case the event space Γ is given by

$$\Gamma = \{E_1, E_2, \ldots, E_n\},$$

where the E_i are the corresponding elementary events. The subsets of Γ correspond to the possible events A. Since according to Section 3.2 every such event A has a canonical representation

$$A = E_{j_1} \cup E_{j_2} \cup \ldots \cup E_{j_m},$$

the probability $p(A)$ of a certain element is given when the probabilities

$$p(E_i), \ i = 1, 2, \ldots, n,$$

of the elementary events are known. According to axiom I (Section 4.5.1) these probabilities must be non-negative numbers.

Moreover, since

$$U = E_1 \cup E_2 \cup \ldots \cup E_n,$$

and $E_i \cap E_j = \emptyset$ for $i \neq j$, the probabilities $p(E_i)$ must, according to axioms II and III, satisfy the condition

$$\sum_{i=1}^{n} p(E_i) = 1.$$

Example   Consider a trial consisting of rolling a die. In this case, there are six elementary events,

$$E_i = \{i \text{ spots showing}\}, \ i = 1, \ldots, 6.$$

The lattice of events corresponds to the power set of $\Gamma = \{E_1, E_2, \ldots, E_6\}$, and therefore contains $2^6 = 64$ elements. Some of these are as follows:

$$G = E_2 \cup E_4 \cup E_6 = \{\text{even number}\},$$
$$P = E_2 \cup E_3 \cup E_5 = \{\text{prime number}\},$$
$$E'_6 = E_1 \cup E_2 \cup E_3 \cup E_4 \cup E_5 = \{\text{not six}\},$$

$V = E_1 \cup E_2 \cup E_3 \cup E_4$
$\quad = \{$number of spots less than or equal to 4$\}$,
$D = E_3 \cup E_4 \cup E_5 \cup E_6$
$\quad = \{$number of spots greater than or equal to 3$\}$,
$F = E_1 \cup E_2 \cup E_3$
$\quad = \{$number of spots less than or equal to 3$\}$.

We can indicate the probabilities of these events if we know the probabilities of the elementary events. However, dice can be chosen such that the probabilities of the elementary events differ substantially. On the other hand, in the case of a fair die it will be possible to assume, for reasons of symmetry, that the six elementary events have the same probability. This is the approach used in the classical theory of probability.

Definition If the hypothesis is made that all elementary events of a probability algebra have the same probability, then the algebra concerned is said to be a *classical probability algebra*.

The classical theory of probability does not give a definition of probability, but rests on the assumption that certain events are equally probable.

If the event space consists of n elementary events E_i, it follows in a classical probability algebra that

$$p(U) = p(E_1 \cup E_2 \cup \ldots \cup E_n) = n \cdot p(E_i)$$

(where i is chosen at random), that is,

$$p(E_i) = \frac{1}{n} \text{ for all } i.$$

If an event A is formed from g elementary events E_{i_1}, E_{i_2}, $\ldots, E_{i_g}$, i.e., if

$$A = E_{i_1} \cup E_{i_2} \cup \ldots \cup E_{i_g},$$

it follows that

$$p(A) = \sum_{\lambda=1}^{g} p(E_{i_\lambda}) = \frac{g}{n}.$$

It follows directly from the above representation of A that

$$E_{i_\lambda} \subset A \quad \text{for} \quad \lambda = 1, 2, \ldots, g,$$

i.e., that the occurrence of the elementary event E_{i_λ} is always followed by the occurrence of the event A. E_{i_λ} is then called an elementary event *favourable to A*. In view of the unambiguity of the canonical representation of A, there are exactly g elementary events favourable to A. We obtain, therefore, the following theorem.

Theorem In a classical probability algebra, the probability of an event A is equal to the quotient of the number g of elementary events favourable to A, and the number n of elementary events.

This theorem reduces the calculation of a probability to a problem in the theory of combinations.

For the case of rolling a die, the classical theory of probability requires

$$p(E_i) = \frac{1}{6} \quad (i = 1, 2, \ldots, 6).$$

We find, therefore, for the compound events mentioned above:

$$p(G) = \frac{1}{2}, \qquad p(P) = \frac{1}{2}, \qquad p(E_6') = \frac{5}{6},$$

$$p(V) = \frac{2}{3}, \qquad p(D) = \frac{2}{3}, \qquad p(F) \;\; = \frac{1}{2}.$$

In addition:

$$p(E_6' \cap G) = \frac{1}{3}, \qquad k(E_6', G) = \frac{\frac{1}{3}}{\frac{5}{6} \cdot \frac{1}{2}} = \frac{4}{5} < 1;$$

$$p(V \cap G) \;\; = \frac{1}{3}, \qquad k(V, G) \;\; = \frac{\frac{1}{3}}{\frac{2}{3} \cdot \frac{1}{2}} = 1;$$

$$p(P \cap G') = \frac{1}{3}, \qquad k(P, G') = \frac{\frac{1}{3}}{\frac{1}{2} \cdot \frac{1}{2}} = \frac{4}{3} > 1.$$

In particular, the events V and G are independent. As shown by the other two results, the effect coefficient of a pair of events can be larger or smaller than 1, a fact which also follows from the definition of this coefficient.

Finally, we return to Problem 65, which will now be considered in the light of probability calculus.

Three players each in turn draw a card from a pack of 36* and return the card immediately. Thus, such a triple draw, i.e., three particular cards in a certain sequence, is an elementary event.

The events in which we are interested are:

$A = \{$player Alfred draws a red card$\}$,

$B = \{$player Bruno draws a red card$\}$,

$C = \{$player Caesar draws a red card$\}$,

$R = A \cap B \cap C = \{$all players draw red cards$\}$,

$S = A' \cap B' \cap C' = \{$all players draw black cards$\}$,

$G = (A \cap B \cap C) \cup (A' \cap B' \cap C')$

$\qquad = \{$all players draw cards of the same colour$\}$.

Let us assume that we are concerned with a classical probability algebra. Then every elementary event has the probability

$$p(E_i) = \left(\frac{1}{36}\right)^3.$$

It follows that:

$$p(A) = \frac{18}{36} \cdot \frac{36}{36} \cdot \frac{36}{36} = \frac{1}{2},$$

and hence also

$$p(B) = p(C) = \frac{1}{2};$$

$$p(A \cap B) = \frac{18}{36} \cdot \frac{18}{36} \cdot \frac{36}{36} = \frac{1}{4};$$

$$p_B(A) = \frac{p(A \cap B)}{p(B)} = \frac{\frac{1}{4}}{\frac{1}{2}} = \frac{1}{2}.$$

*The Swiss card game Jass is played with a pack of 36 cards.

We note that $p_B(A) = p(A)$, i.e., the two events A and B are mutually independent. Furthermore:

$$p(R) = p(S) = \frac{18}{36}\cdot\frac{18}{36}\cdot\frac{18}{36} = \frac{1}{8}.$$

R and S are mutually exclusive events:

$$p(G) = p(R\cup S) = p(R)+p(S) = \frac{1}{8}+\frac{1}{8} = \frac{1}{4}.$$

On the other hand, A and B are events which are not mutually exclusive:

$$p(A\cup B) = p(A)+p(B)-p(A\cap B) = \frac{1}{2}+\frac{1}{2}-\frac{1}{4} = \frac{3}{4}.$$

In connection with this example, the following special relation should be noted:

$$p(A\cap B\cap C) = p[A\cap(B\cap C)] = p_{B\cap C}(A)\cdot p(B\cap C)$$
$$= p_{B\cap C}(A)\cdot p_C(B)\cdot p(C).$$

However, in this example,

$$p(A\cap B\cap C) = p(R) = \left(\tfrac{1}{2}\right)^3$$

and

$$p(A)\cdot p(B)\cdot p(C) = \left(\tfrac{1}{2}\right)^3,$$

i.e., we have

$$p(A\cap B\cap C) = p(A)\cdot p(B)\cdot p(C),$$

a result which obviously characterizes a special relationship between the events A, B and C, since in general

$$p(A)\cdot p(B)\cdot p(C) \neq p_{B\cap C}(A)\cdot p_C(B)\cdot p(C).$$

Definition   Three events A_i $(i = 1, 2, 3)$ are called *completely independent* if the relations

$$p(A_i\cap A_j) = p(A_i)\cdot p(A_j) \quad \text{for} \quad i \neq j,$$

and

$$p(A_1\cap A_2\cap A_3) = p(A_1)\cdot p(A_2)\cdot p(A_3)$$

are satisfied.

Complete independence means that A_1, A_2, A_3 are independent in pairs and, at the same time, each is independent of the intersection of the two others. This is the case for the events A, B and C in our example.

For complete independence, all conditions of the definition are, in fact, necessary, since from the pair-wise independence it is not possible to deduce that any one event is independent of the intersection of the remaining two. This can be shown by means of the following example.

Example Let us consider the probability algebra associated with throwing two dice.

$A = \{$the first die shows an even number of spots$\}$,

$B = \{$the second die shows an odd number of spots$\}$,

$C = \{$both dice show either even or odd numbers of spots$\}$.

In this case it is obvious that

$$p(A) = p(B) = p(C) = \frac{1}{2},$$

$$p(A \cap B) = p(B \cap C) = p(C \cap A) = \frac{1}{4},$$

so that the three events are independent in pairs. However, we have

$$p(A \cap B \cap C) = 0,$$

so that, when A and B occur, C is impossible.

4.7 EXAMPLES OF THE CALCULUS OF PROBABILITY

4.7.1 *Finite probability algebras*

Problem 66 (The problem of the Chevalier de Méré.) Which is more probable:

(a) to throw at least one six in four throws with one die;

(b) to throw at least one double six in 24 throws with two dice?

We shall deal with the two problems (a) and (b) separately.

(a) *The probability of throwing at least one six in four throws with one die.* Four throws with one die can be realized by one throw of four numbered dice thrown together. The event space Γ_1 contains $6^4 = 1296$ elementary events. Each elementary event is characterized by a 4-sample of the set $\{1, \ldots, 6\}$ with repetitions (see p. 42). If we deal with the problem from the viewpoint of classical probability theory, all elementary events are equally probable; i.e., each elementary event has the probability $1/1296$. Assuming that

$$A_i = \{\text{the } i\text{-th die shows a six}\},$$

then we have to calculate the probability

$$p(A_1 \cup A_2 \cup A_3 \cup A_4).$$

First solution: Use of the inclusion and exclusion formula.

$$p(A_1 \cup A_2 \cup A_3 \cup A_4)$$
$$= \sum_{i=1}^{4} p(A_i) - \sum_{i<j}^{4} p(A_i \cap A_j)$$
$$+ \sum_{i<j<k}^{4} p(A_i \cap A_j \cap A_k) - p(A_1 \cap A_2 \cap A_3 \cap A_4).$$

In this,

$$p(A_1) = \frac{1 \cdot 6 \cdot 6 \cdot 6}{6 \cdot 6 \cdot 6 \cdot 6} = \frac{1}{6}.$$

(The first die shows a six, the scores on the other dice being irrelevant.) We also have

$$p(A_i) = \frac{1}{6} \quad \text{for all } i,$$

$$p(A_1 \cap A_2) = \frac{1 \cdot 1 \cdot 6 \cdot 6}{6 \cdot 6 \cdot 6 \cdot 6},$$

$$p(A_i \cap A_j) = \frac{1}{36} \quad \text{for all } i < j.$$

Finally,

$$p(A_i \cap A_j \cap A_k) = \frac{1 \cdot 1 \cdot 1 \cdot 6}{6 \cdot 6 \cdot 6 \cdot 6} = \frac{1}{216} \quad \text{for all } i < j < k.$$

Since $A_1 \cap A_2 \cap A_3 \cap A_4$ is an elementary event, it follows that

$$p(A_1 \cup A_2 \cup A_3 \cup A_4) = 4.\frac{1}{6} - 6.\frac{1}{36} + 4.\frac{1}{216} - \frac{1}{1296}$$
$$= 0{\cdot}5177 \ldots .$$

It should also be mentioned that the events A_i ($i = 1, 2, 3, 4$) are independent of each other, since, when $i \neq j$,

$$p_{A_i}(A_j) = \frac{p(A_i \cap A_j)}{p(A_i)} = \frac{1}{6}, \text{ i.e., } p_{A_i}(A_j) = p(A_j),$$

and so

$$p(A_i \cap A_j) = p(A_i) . p(A_j).$$

Second solution: Use of the negation.
For the required probability we have

$$p(A_1 \cup A_2 \cup A_3 \cup A_4) = 1 - p((A_1 \cup A_2 \cup A_3 \cup A_4)')$$
$$= 1 - p(A_1' \cap A_2' \cap A_3' \cap A_4').$$

However,

$$A_1' \cap A_2' \cap A_3' \cap A_4' = \{\text{no die shows a six}\},$$

and therefore

$$p(A_1' \cap A_2' \cap A_3' \cap A_4') = \frac{5.5.5.5}{6.6.6.6} = \frac{625}{1296}.$$

It follows then, that

$$p(A_1 \cup A_2 \cup A_3 \cup A_4) = 1 - \frac{625}{1296} = \frac{671}{1296}.$$

Note: In this example, the four events A_i' are completely independent; in particular, they satisfy the relation

$$p(A_1' \cap A_2' \cap A_3' \cap A_4') = p(A_1') . P(A_2') . p(A_3') . p(A_4').$$

(b) *The probability of throwing at least one double six in 24 throws of two dice.* Again, the trial can be realized by throwing simultaneously 24 pairs of dice. The dice of a pair are numbered, and also the pairs of dice are distinct. The event space Γ_2 consists of 36^{24} elementary events. One pair of dice yields 36 different possibilities and each elementary event characterizes a 24-sample (with repetitions) of a set of order 36 (see p. 42).

Using once more the classical theory of probability, each elementary event has the probability $1/36^{24}$.

We introduce the following events:

$$B_i = \{\text{double six with the } i\text{-th pair}\}.$$

It follows directly that

$$p(B_1) = \frac{1 \cdot 36 \cdot 36 \cdot 36 \ldots 36}{36 \cdot 36 \cdot 36 \cdot 36 \ldots 36} = \frac{1}{36},$$

$$p(B_i) = \frac{1}{36} \quad \text{for all } i.$$

The probability we are required to find is

$$p(B_1 \cup B_2 \cup B_3 \cup \ldots \cup B_{24}).$$

We shall calculate this using the second of the two methods used above, i.e. by calculating the probability of the negation of the event.

$$\begin{aligned}
p(B_1 \cup B_2 \cup \ldots \cup B_{24}) &= 1 - p\big((B_1 \cup B_2 \cup \ldots \cup B_{24})'\big) \\
&= 1 - p(B'_1 \cap B'_2 \cap \ldots \cap B'_{24}) \\
&= 1 - \left(\frac{35}{36}\right)^{24} = 0 \cdot 491.
\end{aligned}$$

It is easily seen that in this example we again have

$$\begin{aligned}
p(B'_1 \cap B'_2 \cap \ldots \cap B'_{24}) &= p(B'_1) \cdot p(B'_2) \ldots p(B'_{24}) \\
&= [p(B'_1)]^{24}.
\end{aligned}$$

The two events

$$C_1 = A_1 \cup A_2 \cup A_3 \cup A_4 \quad \text{and} \quad C_2 = B_1 \cup B_2 \cup \ldots \cup B_{24}$$

belong to different event spaces. Although the corresponding probabilities can be compared, they cannot be used for calculation at this stage: all we can do with the probabilities is to compare them.

We can now answer the question posed by the Chevalier de Méré: the event C_1 in the event space Γ_1 is somewhat more likely than the event C_2 in the event space Γ_2.

Note: Let Γ be any event space and A an element of the corresponding probability calculus; $p(A)$ denotes the probability of A. It is now possible to combine n trials over Γ to form a single new trial (e.g. rolling a die n times) and so obtain a trial over the event space

$$\Gamma^* = \underbrace{\Gamma \times \Gamma \times \Gamma \times \ldots \times \Gamma.}_{n \text{ factors}}$$

The compound event consisting of the occurrence of event A n times, is denoted by $A^{(n)}$; it corresponds to a subset of Γ^*.

It follows that

$$p(A^{(n)}) = [p(A)]^n.$$

Problem (b) can be interpreted as follows: in the event space Γ which contains the possible throws for two ordered dice, we consider the event $B = \{\text{double six}\}$. Then,

$$p(C_2') = p(B^{(24)'}) = [p(B')]^{24},$$

and hence

$$p(C_2) = 1 - [1 - p(B)]^{24}.$$

Problem 67 What is the probability of two people of a group of n sharing the same birthday?

This problem may also be formulated as follows: Each of n persons has a tear-off calendar. Each tears off one leaf. How great is the likelihood of two persons tearing off the same 'date'.

The event space here consists of 365^n elementary events, namely the n-samples with repetitions of a set of order 365. We introduce the event

$A = \{\text{at least two persons tear off the same date}\}$.

We denote the probability of A by $p_n(A)$, indicating that this probability depends on the number n of persons participating in the trial. We obtain

$$p_n(A) = 1 - p_n(A') = 1 - \frac{365 . 364 . 363 \ldots (365 - n + 1)}{365 . 365 . 365 \ldots 365}.$$

Here, the negation is easier to calculate, since it is only necessary to solve the combinatorial problem of finding the number of elementary events in which n different dates have been torn off.

The probability $p_n(A)$ is given in the following table, taken from *Introduction to Finite Mathematics* by Kemeny, Snell, and Thompson. These numbers provide an indication of what the odds would be in a wager. The change from 'odds against' to 'odds on' occurs between $n = 22$ and $n = 23$.

n	$p_n(A)$	$p_n(A):p_n(A')$
5	0·027	
10	0·117	
15	0·253	
20	0·411	70:100
25	0·569	132:100
30	0·706	242:100
40	0·891	819:100
50	0·970	3300:100
60	0·994	16900:100
150		$4·5.10^{17}:100$
365	1	

Problem 68   Suppose n men each place a visiting card into a hat. Each draws one card. What is the probability that none draws his own card?

The event space Γ contains $n!$ elementary events, namely all possible permutations of the n visiting cards amongst the n men. Every distribution corresponds to a certain permutation of the n cards. We wish to find the probability of the event

$$B = \{\text{permutation without fixed points}\}.$$

We introduce the events

$$A_i = \{\text{the } i\text{-th man draws his own card}\}.$$

It follows that

$$p(A_i) = \frac{(n-1)!}{n!} = \frac{1}{n};$$

$$p(A_i \cap A_j) = \frac{(n-2)!}{n!} = \frac{1}{n(n-1)}, \, i < j;$$

$$p(A_i \cap A_j \cap A_k) = \frac{(n-3)!}{n!} = \frac{1}{n(n-1)(n-2)}, \, i < j < k.$$

The inclusion and exclusion formula therefore gives:

$$
\begin{aligned}
p(B) &= p((A_1 \cup A_2 \cup \ldots \cup A_n)') \\
&= 1 - p(A_1 \cup A_2 \cup \ldots \cup A_n) \\
&= 1 - \sum_{i=1}^{n} p(A_i) + \sum_{i<j}^{n} p(A_i \cap A_j) - \ldots \\
&= 1 - \frac{n}{n} + \binom{n}{2}\frac{1}{n(n-1)} - \binom{n}{3}\frac{1}{n(n-1)(n-2)} + \ldots \\
&= 1 - 1 + \frac{1}{2!} - \frac{1}{3!} + \ldots + (-1)^n \frac{1}{n!} \\
&= \sum_{k=0}^{n} \frac{(-1)^k}{k!}.
\end{aligned}
$$

This is another version of the Bernoulli-Euler problem of the interchanged letters. The probability that none of the men draws his own visiting card, decreases with the number of men participating in the trial. However, it cannot become less than $1/e$, since

$$
\lim_{n \to \infty} p(B) = \sum_{k=0}^{\infty} \frac{(-1)^k}{k!} = \frac{1}{e}.
$$

Problem 69 Suppose n men drop their visiting cards into a hat. Each draws one card. What is the probability that exactly r of them draw their own?

We require the probability of the event

$$C = \{\text{permutation with exactly } r \text{ fixed points}\}.$$

If A_i are the same events as in Problem 68, the inclusion and exclusion formula gives

$$
p(C) = \sum_{k=0}^{n-r} (-1)^k \binom{k+r}{k} \Phi_{k+r}^{(n)}(A),
$$

where

$$
\begin{aligned}
\Phi_\rho^{(n)} &= \sum p(A_{i_1} \cap A_{i_2} \cap \ldots \cap A_{i_\rho}) \\
&= \binom{n}{\rho}\frac{(n-\rho)!}{n!}.
\end{aligned}
$$

Thus we have for $p(C)$,

$$p(C) = \frac{1}{n!} \sum_{k=0}^{n-r} (-1)^k \binom{k+r}{k} \binom{n}{k+r} (n-k-r)!$$

$$= \frac{1}{r!} \sum_{k=0}^{n-r} (-1)^k \frac{1}{k!}.$$

With fixed r and increasing n, the probability $p(C)$ is again decreasing but cannot drop below the value

$$\lim_{n \to \infty} p(C) = \frac{1}{r!} \cdot \frac{1}{e}.$$

Problem 70   100 people are queuing to obtain admission to an exhibition for which the entrance fee is 1s. Of these 100 people 60 have only one-shilling pieces and 40 have only two-shilling pieces. No money is available at the turnstile until the sale of tickets commences. What is the probability that the sale proceeds without stoppage, i.e., that whenever a person having only a two-shilling piece arrives at the turnstile, there is change available?

We shall deal with the general case. Let n be the number of persons with one-shilling pieces and m the number of persons with two-shilling pieces; $n > m$.

Every permutation of the $n+m$ buyers is an elementary event. Thus, there are $(n+m)!$ elementary events. Each has the probability

$$\frac{1}{(n+m)!},$$

again using the assumptions made in the classical theory of probability. If we denote every buyer by the coin with which he pays, then corresponding to every elementary event we have a sales sequence V such as

$$1112212121121 \ldots 1221,$$

which may be regarded as a compound event. It is the combination of all the elementary events leading to this sales sequence. There are $n! \, m!$ of these, since the '1's may be

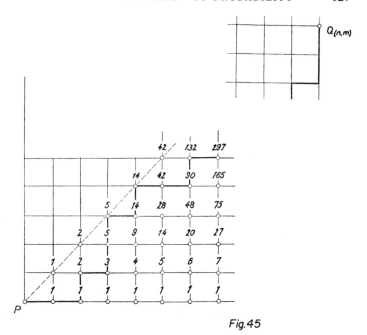

Fig.45

interchanged with themselves and the '2's may also be interchanged with themselves, without altering the sequence. Thus, every sales sequence has the probability

$$p(V) = \frac{n!\,m!}{(n+m)!}.$$

In order to clarify the argument, we shall represent the possible sales sequences graphically. A horizontal unit is associated with every '1' and a vertical unit with every '2'.

Every sales sequence is represented by a path which can extend either to the right or upwards, and contains altogether n horizontal and m vertical units. All paths start at $P(0, 0)$ and end at $Q(n, m)$ (Figure 45). A sales sequence which does not result in a stoppage corresponds to a path which does not cross the dotted line.

We are interested in the compound event which is the

combination of all sales sequences of this kind. It is sufficient to determine the number of sequences, because every sales sequence has the same probability and any two random sales sequences are mutually exclusive. In order to find this number, we first find how many permissible paths, $A(j, k)$, pass through the grid point (j, k) (Figure 45). We are interested in the number which terminate at Q. Since a path can be extended only to the right or upwards, it follows that

$$A(j,k) = A(j-1, k) + A(j, k-1) \text{ for } j > k,$$
$$A(k, k) = A(k, k-1),$$
$$A(j, 0) = 1,$$
$$A(j, 1) = j.$$

If we try to express the smaller numbers occurring in Figure 45 in terms of the coefficients in a Pascal triangle, we obtain

$$A(j, k) = \binom{j+k-1}{k} - \binom{j+k-1}{k-2} = \frac{j-k+1}{j+k+1}\binom{j+k+1}{k}.$$

It can easily be confirmed that the right-hand term satisfies the four relations above.

After this preparation we return to our probability problem. The number in which we are interested is

$$A(n, m) = \frac{n-m+1}{n+m+1}\binom{n+m+1}{m}.$$

If T is the event {sale without stoppage}, it follows that

$$p(T) = A(n, m)p(V) = \frac{n-m+1}{n+m+1}\binom{n+m+1}{m}\frac{n!\,m!}{(n+m)!}$$

$$= \frac{n-m+1}{n+1}.$$

With the numerical values given, we have

$$p(T) = \frac{60-40+1}{60+1} = \frac{21}{61}.$$

An elegant solution of Problem 70 by means of reflections is given by A.M. and I.M. Yaglom in *Challenging Mathematical Problems with Elementary Solutions, Vol.* 1.

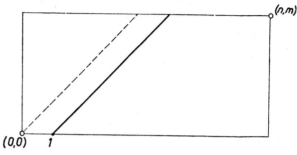

Fig.46

Problem 71 An urn contains n white and m black balls. Balls are drawn from the urn at random and one at a time, without being replaced. What is the probability that at a certain instant, the number of white balls drawn is equal to the number of black?

If at one certain instant equal numbers of black and white balls have been drawn, then this will be regarded as a balanced draw. If $m = n$, a balance is achieved at least by the end of the draw. In this special case, the probability is equal to one. We shall therefore assume that $n > m$. The problem is related to that of Problem 70. The draw of a white ball is represented by a horizontal unit, that of a black ball by a vertical unit. In Figure 46, a complete trial is represented by a path which starts at $(0, 0)$, terminates at (n, m) and proceeds only by steps to the right or upwards. A balance is *never* achieved if the trace avoids the dotted line, i.e., never passes above the solid line. Let G be the event {sequence of draws with balance}. Then

$$p(G) = 1 - p(G') = 1 - \frac{A(n-1, m)}{\binom{n+m}{m}}$$

$$= 1 - \frac{\frac{n-m}{n+m}\binom{n+m}{m}}{\binom{n+m}{m}} = \frac{2m}{n+m}.$$

4.7.2   *Infinite probability algebras*

Problem 72   A watch is allowed to run down. What is the probability that the minute hand will stop between 3 and 6?

Every interval of the circle characterizes an event, an element of the lattice of events. It is proposed to associate congruent intervals with the same probability. This is a hypothesis of the classical theory of probability. Accordingly, the measure of probability is proportional to the length of arc of the interval characterizing the event:

$$p(A) = \frac{l(A)}{l(U)} = \frac{l(A)}{2\pi}.$$

In particular, according to this convention, the event

$$E = \{\text{minute hand is between 3 and 6}\}$$

is associated with the probability

$$p(E) = \frac{\pi/2}{2\pi} = \frac{1}{4}.$$

Note, however, the remarks following Problem 76.

Problem 73   How many sultanas must there be in a cake weighing 1 kg in order to ensure that the probability of there being at least one sultana in each piece weighing 50 g is 0·99?

We shall assume that there are n numbered sultanas in the cake (n to be determined). An event is characterized by a certain distribution of sultanas in the cake. We allow two or more sultanas to be in the same place, and so our model is only a rough realization of the actual distribution of the sultanas.

We shall now consider a certain piece of the cake weighing 50 g and the event

$$A_i = \{\text{the sultana with number } i \text{ is in this selected piece of cake}\}.$$

The hypothesis itself suggests that we shall attach equal probability to a sultana being present in pieces of cake of the same weight. Accordingly, the probability is proportional to the corresponding volume:

$$p(A_i) = \frac{v(P)}{v(U)} = \frac{1}{20} \text{ for all } i.$$

It now follows for the event

$$R = \{\text{at least one sultana in the piece } P\}$$

that

$$p(R) = 1 - p(A_1' \cap A_2' \cap \ldots \cap A_n')$$
$$= 1 - p_{A_1' \cap A_2' \cap \ldots \cap A_{n-1}'}(A_n') \cdot p(A_1' \cap A_2' \cap \ldots \cap A_{n-1}')$$
$$= 1 - p(A_n') \cdot p(A_1' \cap A_2' \cap \ldots \cap A_{n-1}'),$$

because the event A_n' is obviously independent of any combination of the events A_i ($i = 1, 2, \ldots, n-1$).

It follows finally that:

$$p(R) = 1 - p(A_1') \cdot p(A_2') \ldots p(A_n') = 1 - [1 - p(A_1)]^n$$
$$= 1 - \left(\frac{19}{20}\right)^n.$$

Putting $p(R) = 0 \cdot 99$, we obtain $n = 89 \cdot 7$, that is, 90 sultanas are needed.

Problem 74   A line segment is divided into three parts by two points chosen at random. What is the probability that a triangle can be formed from the resulting three segments?

First solution   The line segment is assumed to be the interval [0, 1] on the x-axis. Hence, every division may be characterized by two numbers ξ and η between 0 and 1 (Figure 47).

(a) Assuming that $\xi < \eta$, the conditions that must be satisfied before a triangle can be formed are

$$\xi < 1 - \xi \Rightarrow 0 < \xi < \tfrac{1}{2},$$
$$\xi > 1 - \eta \Rightarrow \tfrac{1}{2} < \eta < 1,$$
$$\eta - \xi < \xi + 1 - \eta \Rightarrow \eta - \xi < \tfrac{1}{2}.$$

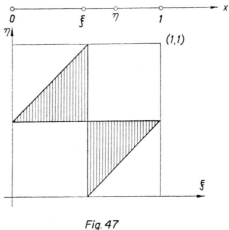

Fig. 47

These may be summarized as follows:

$$0 < \xi < \tfrac{1}{2} < \eta < 1 \quad \text{and} \quad \eta - \xi < \tfrac{1}{2}.$$

(b) If $\eta < \xi$, it follows correspondingly that

$$0 < \eta < \tfrac{1}{2} < \xi < 1 \quad \text{and} \quad \xi - \eta < \tfrac{1}{2}.$$

The ordered pair of numbers (ξ, η) determines a point in the plane. The event space consists therefore of the points within the square $0 < \xi < 1, 0 < \eta < 1$. As a probability measure we must introduce an additive set function for which this square has measure 1; this can be done in infinitely many ways. An obvious way is to associate the interval pair $(d\xi, d\eta)$ at each point with the same probability. This means that the probability measure is proportional to the area measure of the plane. The event

$$D = \{\text{a triangle can be formed}\}$$

is characterized by the shaded zones. It follows, therefore, that:

$$p(D) = \frac{A(D)}{A(U)} = \tfrac{1}{4}.$$

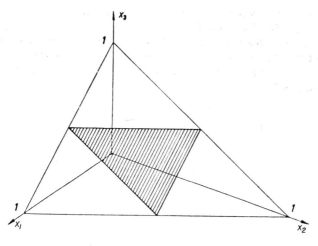

Fig.48

Second solution   Let the segment have length 1, and the three parts have lengths x_1, x_2, x_3. It is therefore true for any random division that

$$x_i > 0, \qquad x_1 + x_2 + x_3 = 1.$$

The conditions for the formation of a triangle are:

$$x_1 + x_2 > x_3, \quad x_1 + x_2 = 1 - x_3 > x_3,$$
$$x_2 + x_3 > x_1, \quad x_2 + x_3 = 1 - x_1 > x_1,$$
$$x_3 + x_1 > x_2, \quad x_3 + x_1 = 1 - x_2 > x_2.$$

Thus we require that $x_i < \frac{1}{2}$ for all *i*. The part of the plane $x_1 + x_2 + x_3 = 1$ shaded in Figure 48 corresponds to the solution set of these three inequalities. Again assuming that the probability should be proportional to the area, we find once more that

$$p(D) = \frac{A(D)}{A(U)} = \tfrac{1}{4}.$$

It should be noted that the probability measure is not given in the problem. In this example, we postulate that equal probabilities should be attached to events associated with

Euclidean-congruent regions. This assumption is made in analogy with the classical theory of probability. However, the hyperbolic area measure could be taken equally well as our additive set function. Bertrand's paradox arises from our freedom to base the same probability problem on different measures.*

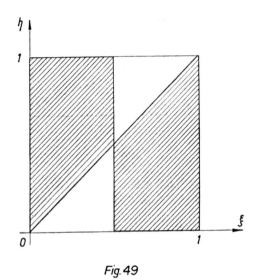

Fig. 49

Problem 75   A stick is broken at random into two parts, and the larger section is again broken at random into two parts. What is the probability that a triangle can be formed from the three parts? (Note that the conditions concerning the division of the stick differ from those of Problem 74.)

Here the event space is limited compared with that of Problem 74. We have the cases

(a) $\xi < \frac{1}{2}$, $\xi < \eta < 1$;
(b) $\xi > \frac{1}{2}$, $0 < \eta < \xi$.

*See, for example, *Probability, Statistics and Truth* by R. von Mises, George Allen and Unwin, London, 1957.

These give as event space the points inside the shaded region in Figure 49. Since the event D has remained unchanged, it follows that

$$p(D) = \frac{A(D)}{A(U)} = \tfrac{1}{3}.$$

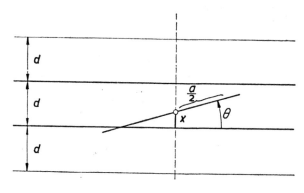

Fig. 50

Problem 76 (Buffon's Needle Problem) Parallel lines are drawn in a plane at a distance d apart. A needle of length a is allowed to drop onto this plane. What is the probability that the needle will intersect one of the lines?

The position of the needle may be fixed by the coordinates of its centre and by an angle θ, defined as follows: θ is the angle through which the straight lines would have to be rotated in the positive sense in order to be parallel to the needle (Figure 50). We assume that all points of the plane are equally likely to be covered by the centre of the needle. Thus, we may first assume that the centre is in the band formed by two certain parallel lines.

Whether these lines are intersected by the needle depends only on the distance between them and not on which perpendicular the centre of the needle is located. Hence, we may assume that the centre is located on the dotted perpendicular (Figure 50), so that only the ordinate of the needle centre need be taken into consideration. The position of the needle is now described by x and θ. The event $S = \{\text{needle intersects}\}$ is characterized by the inequalities

$$0 \leqslant x \leqslant \frac{a}{2}\sin\theta, \qquad d - \frac{a}{2}\sin\theta \leqslant x \leqslant d.$$

$\underbrace{\qquad\qquad\qquad}_{\text{Event } S_1} \qquad \underbrace{\qquad\qquad\qquad\qquad}_{\text{Event } S_2}$

According to our assumptions, the event space is represented by the rectangle

$$0 \leqslant x \leqslant d, \qquad 0 \leqslant \theta \leqslant \pi.$$

The event S is represented in Figure 51 by the shaded regions. We shall now assume that congruent sets in the event space have the same probabilities, i.e. that the probability of an event is again proportional to the area of the corresponding region. The cases (α), (β) and (γ), shown in Figure 51, must be distinguished.

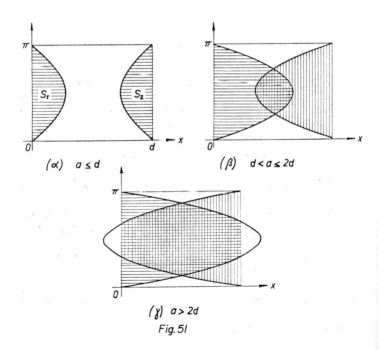

$(\alpha) \quad a \leq d$

$(\beta) \quad d < a \leq 2d$

$(\gamma) \quad a > 2d$

Fig. 51

We have, for the event S:

$$p(S_1 \cup S_2) = p(S_1) + p(S_2) - p(S_1 \cap S_2).$$

In the case (α), $S_1 \cap S_2 = \emptyset$, while in the cases (β) and (γ) $S_1 \cap S_2 \neq \emptyset$. We shall deal only with case (α), and leave the calculations for cases (β) and (γ) to the reader.

$$p(S_1 \cup S_2) = p(S_1) + p(S_2) = \frac{A(S_1) + A(S_2)}{A(U)}$$

$$= \frac{2\frac{a}{2} \int_0^\pi \sin \theta \, d\theta}{\pi d} = \frac{2a}{\pi d}.$$

Remarks 1. It should be stressed that in an infinite probability algebra one cannot conclude from $p(A) = 1$ that A is the certain event. There are sets of measure zero differing from $\emptyset$. For example, in the needle problem, the set $\{\theta = 45°\}$ has obviously zero measure. It is the set corresponding to the positions in which the needle has its direction fixed by the angle $45°$. In the event space, this set is represented by a line parallel to the x-axis, which must be given the area measure zero. We see from this remark that

$p(A) = 1 \Rightarrow A$ is an almost certain event,

$p(A) = 0 \Rightarrow A$ is an almost impossible event.

In Problem 72, the event corresponding to a single point on the circle would also have zero probability, although it is not impossible that the point of the hand should stop exactly at this point. However, this event is 'almost impossible'.

2. Buffon's problem makes it possible to elaborate a statistical method for the numerical determination of π. Suppose the trial is carried out n times under the condition (α), and that the needle intersects the parallel lines on g occasions. Then g/n is the relative frequency {needle intersects} for the event and thus an approximation to the number $p(S)$. It follows, therefore, that

$$\frac{\pi}{2} = \frac{a}{d \cdot p(S)} \simeq \frac{a}{d} \cdot \frac{n}{g}.$$

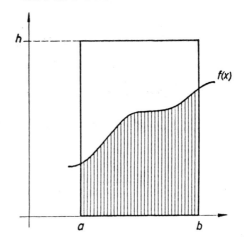

Fig.52

Thus we can obtain an approximation to π by means of the Monte-Carlo method.*

In a similar way, we can find an approximate value for the definite integral

$$\int_a^b f(x)dx.$$

If a small ball is allowed to drop onto the rectangle in Figure 52 so that the congruent areas are hit with the same probability, the probability that the shaded zone is hit is

$$p(S) = \frac{\int_a^b f(x)dx}{h(b-a)} \quad .$$

An approximation to this probability can now be obtained by finding the relative frequency of success in a series of trials.**

Further exercises in the calculus of probability can be found in [3], [4], [5], [11], and [15].

*The application of statistical methods to non-statistical problems.

**Instead of setting up a physical experiment, one can use a table of random numbers to generate the coordinates of the point where the ball can be assumed to have dropped.

5

SWITCHING ALGEBRA

The algebra of circuits, or switching algebra, is an application of Boolean algebra which has been developed only recently and is a topic which lies on the boundary between pure mathematics and theoretical electrical engineering. The core of this new application was developed by a group of researchers in the USA, consisting of mathematicians and electrical engineers, a combination of interests which is rarely found in Europe. This intensive research in the United States into the algebra of circuits is closely linked with the enormous development of computer techniques which has recently taken place.

C. E. Shannon was the first to introduce circuit algebra as a method for dealing algebraically with relay circuits,* and this at a time (1938) when there were no large computers. However, extensive contact** circuits existed in telecommunication and remote control installations. The increasing complexity of these installations necessitated a theoretical investigation into the structure of contact networks and the practical utilization of the results. Thus, switching algebra grew directly from its applications. The digital computer, which contains large numbers of logic circuits in a small space, opened up a wide field of applications to switching algebra and secured its recognition as a part of modern mathematics.

5.1 THE FOUNDATIONS OF SWITCHING ALGEBRA

Theoretically, switching algebra may be approached from the theory of Boolean lattices or from formal logic. Since we

---

*Shannon, C. E., 'Analysis of Relay and Switching Circuits.' *Trans. AIEE,* 57, 1938. Shannon is also regarded as the founder of what is known as *information theory*. This also resulted from telecommunication methods, but today deals with information carriers of all kinds, including language.

**The term *contact* carries essentially the same meaning as *switch*.

already have some acquaintance with Boolean algebra, the former approach will be easier; it is also more suitable for pedagogical reasons. At present, there is no real necessity for the use of much formal logic in school mathematics.

As shown in Section 3.4, finite Boolean lattices having the same order (which is necessarily a power of 2) are mutually isomorphic. The smallest Boolean lattice consists of only the elements O and E. Figure 53 shows the power set model of this smallest lattice $[L, \cup, \cap]$: $L = P(U) = \{\emptyset, U\}$; the symbols $\cup$ and $\cap$ as usual denote the union and intersection of sets.

Making use of the symbols mentioned in Section 2.2, the same lattice can be described as the system

$$S = [\{0, 1\}, +, \cdot].$$

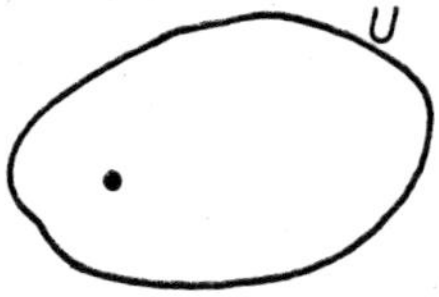

Fig. 53

This trivial Boolean lattice will play a large part in our investigations. Since there are only two different elements, all possible additions and multiplications can be easily inspected. These are summarized in the two tables below which are set out in the manner usually used for truth tables.

Addition			Multiplication		
$x+y = s$			$x.y = p$		
x	y	s	x	y	p
0	0	0	0	0	0
0	1	1	0	1	0
1	0	1	1	0	0
1	1	1	1	1	1

In principle, we have here the value tables of two very simple functions in the two variables x and y.

The formation of the complement corresponds to a function in one variable with the following table.

Complement	
x	x'
0	1
1	0

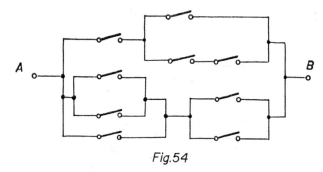

Fig.54

The Boolean lattice S is completely characterized by the value tables of the three functions $s(x, y)$, $p(x, y)$ and $c(x) = x'$.

This abstract Boolean lattice has a further interesting realization in simple 2-terminal circuits, i.e. electrical networks with two terminals (input and output) and which contain only switches. Figure 54 shows the diagram of such a circuit. The only circuit property of interest in our algebra is whether or not current can flow between the end-points of any section of the circuit. In the first case we associate with the section the conductance 1, in the latter the conductance 0. Thus, each section can be associated with one of two values.

This conductance has nothing to do with the physical conductance, the reciprocal resistance. If we wish to stress this particularly, we shall refer to the former as the structural conductance.

In what follows, a section with one switch will be called an *elementary bipole*. With an elementary bipole we associate the indeterminate conductance x; according to the switch position, $x = 1$, or $x = 0$ (see Figure 55).

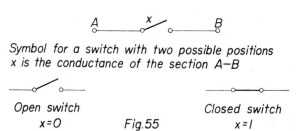

Symbol for a switch with two possible positions
x is the conductance of the section $A–B$

Open switch   Closed switch
$x = 0$ Fig.55 $x = 1$

5.1.1 *Two elementary bipoles in parallel*

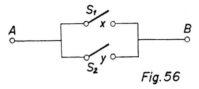

Fig. 56

x = conductance in the branch containing S_1,
y = conductance in the branch containing S_2,
s = conductance of the section A–B.

Current can flow between A and B if either S_1 or S_2 is closed. The OR has here the sense of the Latin *vel*, *i.e.* it is not mutually exclusive (and/or). In logic, this OR link is called a *disjunction*.

We obtain the following conductance table for this combination of switches:

x	y	s
0	0	0
0	1	1
1	0	1
1	1	1

Comparison shows that this is identical to the addition table of the Boolean lattice S.

5.1.2 *Two elementary bipoles in series*

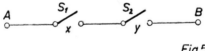

Fig. 57

x = conductance in the branch containing S_1,
y = conductance in the branch containing S_2,
p = conductance in the section A–B.

Current will flow between A and B only if both switches are closed. In logic, this AND combination is called a *conjunction*.

The following conductance values are obtained for the series circuit:

x	y	p
0	0	0
0	1	0
1	0	0
1	1	1

This agrees with the multiplication table for the lattice S.

5.1.3 Negation

Coupled switches may also occur in our 2-terminal circuits. These are switches which are linked in such a way that they change their conductance together. Coupled switches are realized in practice as multiple switches on the same axis or as relays. If two coupled switches open and close together, they have always the same conductance; if one is open when the other is closed, their conductances are complementary. This must always be taken into consideration when denoting the conductance variables.

As an example we shall consider the electromagnetic relay shown in Figure 58. When the relay is energized, the first three (*make*) switches close whilst the fourth (*break*) is open*. If the make contacts have the conductance 1, the break contact has

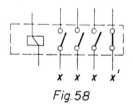

Fig. 58

the conductance 0 and *vice versa*. If we denote the make contact by the conductance variable x, the break contact must always have the opposite value, i.e. x'. We say: the variable x' is formed from x by *negation*.

In this connection it should be stressed that relay contacts are always drawn in circuit diagrams with the contacts in the inoperative positions (relay de-energized, relay coil does not carry current), i.e. make contacts are shown open.

The table for negation follows directly. It agrees with the table for the formation of the complement in the lattice S.

x	x'
0	1
1	0

*By a *make* switch (or contact) we mean one which is open when no current passes through the coil of the electromagnet.

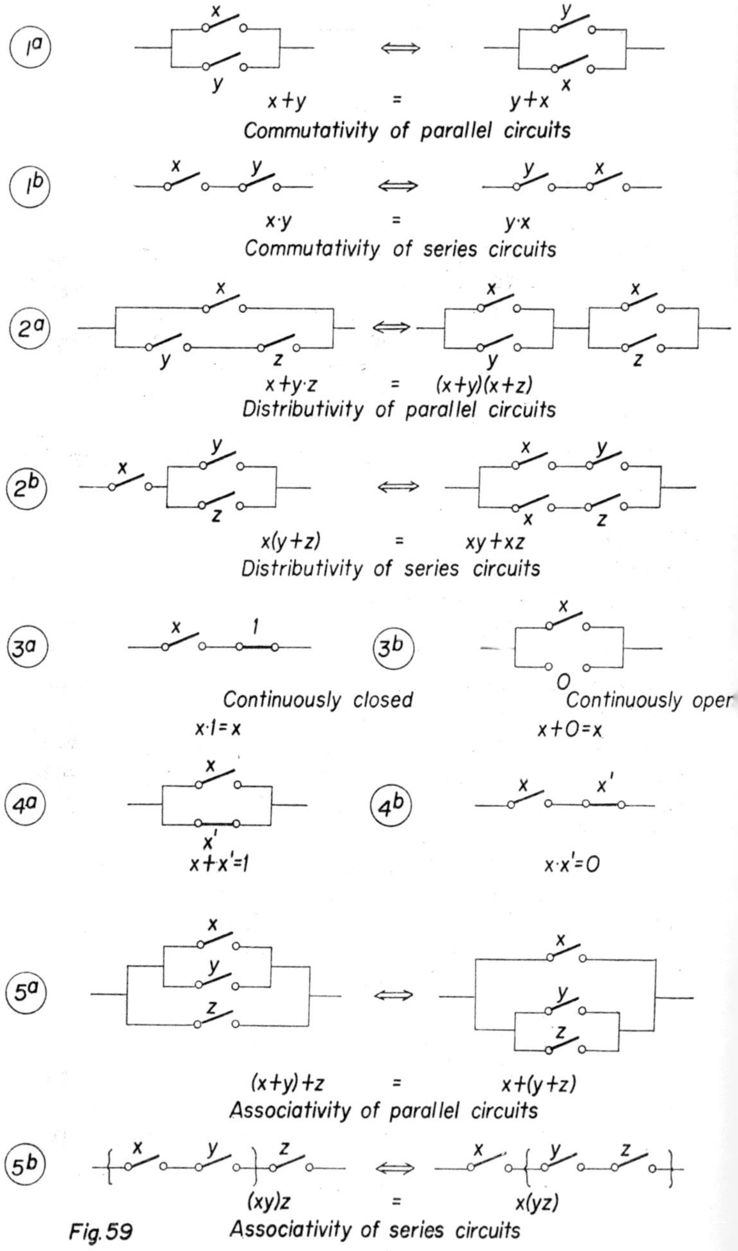
1a
x
y
y
x
x+y = y+x
Commutativity of parallel circuits
1b
x y
y x
x·y = y·x
Commutativity of series circuits
2a
x
y z
x
y
x
z
x+y·z = (x+y)(x+z)
Distributivity of parallel circuits
2b
x
y
z
x y
x z
x(y+z) = xy+xz
Distributivity of series circuits
3a
x 1
Continuously closed
x·1=x
3b
x
0
Continuously oper
x+0=x
4a
x
x'
x+x'=1
4b
x x'
x·x'=0
5a
x
y
z
x
y
z
(x+y)+z = x+(y+z)
Associativity of parallel circuits
5b
x y z
x y z
(xy)z = x(yz)
Associativity of series circuits

Fig. 59

The agreement between the tables for parallel and series circuits and for negation with those for addition, multiplication and the formation of the complement in the Boolean lattice S leads directly to the following theorem.

Theorem The conductance set $\{0, 1\}$ with the operations corresponding to the formation of parallel circuits, series circuits and negation, is a Boolean lattice which is isomorphic to the smallest power set lattice S.

The application of Boolean algebra to this lattice is called switching algebra.

In the following, the combination of conductances by means of parallel and series circuitry will be designated by the operators $+$ and $\cdot$ respectively.

5.2 ILLUSTRATION OF THE LAWS OF SWITCHING ALGEBRA*

The circuits shown in Figure 59 on opposite sides of the equivalence signs are said to be *electrically equivalent*, *i.e.* their conductance behaviours are the same.

5.3 INVESTIGATION OF A SIMPLE SWITCHING CIRCUIT

The following example illustrates the use of switching algebra for the analysis and simplification of a given switching circuit.

We consider three multiple switches S_1, S_2 and S_3, connected in accordance with the circuit diagram shown in Figure 60.

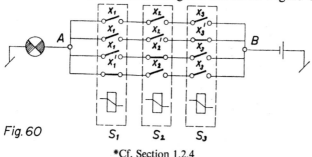

Fig. 60

S_1 S_2 S_3

*Cf. Section 1.2.4

(The switches may be realized by relays.) The lamp lights when the section A–B has the conductance 1. The switches S_1, S_2 and S_3 give three control possibilities for the conductance of the section A–B. Logically, the section A–B is an information converter with three inputs and one output.

Fig.61

Figure 61 shows the section diagrammatically, indicating the three inputs and the one output. We shall call such a circuit a *logical* 3-1 *pole*. The variables x_1, x_2, x_3 characterize the positions of the three switches S_1, S_2, S_3; s is the conductance variable for the section A–B. The arrows indicate the flow of information.

The conductance s depends on the switch positions; it is, therefore, a function of the three variables x_1, x_2 and x_3. From the electrical circuit we immediately obtain the following representation of the switching function:

$$s(x_1, x_2, x_3) = x_1 x_2 x_3 + x_1 x_2 x_3' + x_1 x_2' x_3 + x_1' x_2 x_3.$$

Let us now consider all possible switch positions. Since every switch has two possible positions, the circuit has altogether $2^3 = 8$ switching positions; the complete value table of our switching function contains therefore eight lines.

The sequence we adopt in enumerating the eight switching conditions is, in itself, irrelevant. A uniform arrangement can be achieved by introducing the so-called binary index. If, for example, S_1 and S_2 are operative, but S_3 is not, this position is marked by $x_1 = 1$, $x_2 = 1$, $x_3 = 0$. If these three conductances are regarded as the binary digits of a number, this number will represent the binary index. In our case we have

$$1, 1, 0 \qquad 110_2 = 6_{10}.^*$$

The switch position chosen has the binary index 6.

---

*In future we shall omit the suffix indicating the number base unless there is a risk of misunderstanding.

The following value table for the switching function (x_1, x_2, x_3) contains the switch positions arranged in ascending order of binary indices.

Variable								
x_1	x_2	x_3	Binary index	$x_1 x_2 x_3$	$x_1 x_2 x_3'$	$x_1 x_2' x_3$	$x_1' x_2 x_3$	s
0	0	0	$000 = 0$	0	0	0	0	0
0	0	1	$001 = 1$	0	0	0	0	0
0	1	0	$010 = 2$	0	0	0	0	0
0	1	1	$011 = 3$	0	0	0	1	1
1	0	0	$100 = 4$	0	0	0	0	0
1	0	1	$101 = 5$	0	0	1	0	1
1	1	0	$110 = 6$	0	1	0	0	1
1	1	1	$111 = 7$	1	0	0	0	1

Now, s assumes the value 1 if, and only if, more than one relay has been activated. If the relay is regarded as push-button controlled, this switching circuit represents a means whereby three persons may vote for or against a motion indicating as they do so whether the motion is carried or not.

We have represented this switching function as the sum of four products in which every variable occurs (either directly or negated) exactly once. Such products are called complete conjunctions*. Inspection of the value table shows that each of the complete conjunctions occurring in s assumes the value 1 exactly once. With three variables there are, altogether, $2^3 = 8$ possible complete conjunctions. In the switching function s, only four of these occur; those characterizing the switch positions associated with the conductance 1. We shall refer back to this later.

We shall now use switching algebra in order to simplify our circuit. In this case, we can write:

$$s(x_1, x_2, x_3) = x_1 x_2 x_3 + x_1 x_2 x_3' + x_1 x_2' x_3 + x_1' x_2 x_3$$
$$= (x_1 + x_1')x_2 x_3 + x_1 (x_2' x_3 + x_2 x_3')$$
$$= x_2 x_3 + x_1 (x_2' x_3 + x_2 x_3').$$

This new form of the switching function is represented by a much simpler circuit.

*See Problem 45.

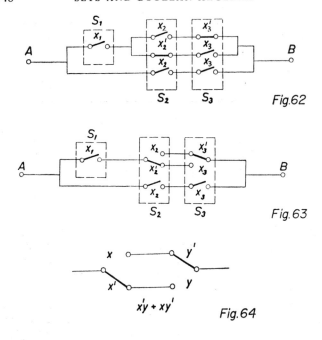

Fig.62

Fig. 63

Fig.64

Compared with the previous circuit, the number of contacts can be reduced from 12 to 7 (see Figure 62). A further simplification is possible by using *transfer* contacts* in S_2 and S_3 (Figure 63).

For later purposes we should stress once more how the term $x'y+xy'$ may be realized by means of transfer contacts; this circuit is shown in Figure 64.

Problem 77 The switching function in Section 5.3 may be transformed into:

$$s(x_1, x_2, x_3) = x_1 x_2 + x_2 x_3 + x_3 x_1 = x_1 x_2 + x_3 (x_1 + x_2).$$

Carry out this transformation and draw the circuit diagram for this representation of the switching function.

---

*A transfer contact is a combination of a make and break contact operating from a single spring. It is also known as a changeover switch.

Compare the number of active contacts in the new circuit with those in the circuits given in the text.

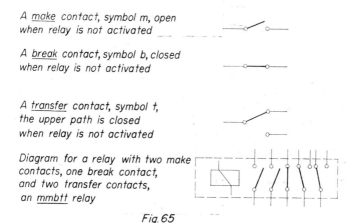

A *make* contact, symbol m, open
when relay is not activated

A *break* contact, symbol b, closed
when relay is not activated

A *transfer* contact, symbol t,
the upper path is closed
when relay is not activated

Diagram for a relay with two make
contacts, one break contact,
and two transfer contacts,
an *mmbtt* relay

Fig. 65

Figure 65 provides a summary of the symbols used for the types of contacts under discussion.

Switching algebra is an important aid in the analysis and synthesis of simple 2-terminal circuits, with the logical $n-1$ pole playing an especially important role. It may be completely described by means of a switching function in n variables.

Analysis implies the examination of an already existing circuit. For, by means of the switching function for the circuit, we are able to give a complete mathematical description of the relation between input and output. Switching algebra then often makes the design of simpler, equivalent circuits possible. In practice, a common problem is that of minimum realization, i.e. of designing a circuit with minimum expenditure. However, according to the technical construction of the switching devices, different items will have to be minimized to secure minimum expenditure, for example, the number of active contacts, or the number of relays.

In the synthesis of circuits the object is to design a circuit with certain properties. We shall see that switching algebra can be used successfully for this purpose also.

5.4   THE LOGICAL 2–1 POLE

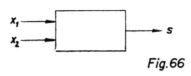

Fig. 66

The logical 2–1 pole is a 2-terminal circuit with two inputs and one output (see Figure 66). Two switches correspond to the inputs, their switching positions being described by the two variables x_1 and x_2. The switching function s describes conditions under which current will flow through the section A–B.

We shall now list all possible types of logical 2–1 poles. A given logical 2–1 pole is characterized by the value table of the switching function $s(x_1, x_2)$.

x_1	x_2	$s(x_1, x_2)$
0	0	ε_1
0	1	ε_2
1	0	ε_3
1	1	ε_4

Since the variables x_1 and x_2 can take exactly two values there are $2^2 = 4$ combinations; these correspond to the possible switch positions. Hence, the value table has four lines.

The functional values ε_i are 0 or 1. The number of different possible logical 2–1 poles is therefore equal to the number of ways in which the values 0 and 1 can be entered in the column of the functional values; it is $2^4 = 16$. Hence, there are sixteen different logical 2–1 poles, although some of them are extremely trivial.

The table printed opposite gives a summary of the 16 possible switching functions in two variables. Again, in view of the distribution of the '1's in the value table, it is worthwhile introducing the binary index. Thus, the table contains the 16 switching functions in 2 variables arranged in ascending binary index. For example, the value distribution 0101 is associated with the binary index 5. Using this value table, we can immediately obtain an algebraic representation of the

Input

x_1 0011
x_2 0101

$$0000 \ s_0 = \qquad\qquad\qquad 0$$

$$0001 \ s_1 = \qquad\qquad\qquad x_1 x_2$$

$$0010 \ s_2 = \qquad\qquad x_1 x_2'$$

$$0011 \ s_3 = \qquad\qquad x_1 x_2' + x_1 x_2 = x_1(x_2' + x_2)$$
$$= x_1$$

$$0100 \ s_4 = \qquad x_1' x_2$$

$$0101 \ s_5 = \qquad x_1' x_2 \qquad + x_1 x_2 = (x_1 + x_1')x_2$$
$$= x_2$$

$$0110 \ s_6 = \qquad x_1' x_2 + x_1 x_2'$$

$$0111 \ s_7 = \qquad x_1' x_2 + x_1 x_2' + x_1 x_2 = (x_1' + x_1)x_2$$
$$+ x_1(x_2' + x_2)$$
$$= x_1 + x_2$$

$$1000 \ s_8 = x_1' x_2'$$

$$1001 \ s_9 = x_1' x_2' \qquad\qquad + x_1 x_2$$

$$1010 \ s_{10} = x_1' x_2' \qquad + x_1 x_2' \qquad = (x_1 + x_1')x_2'$$
$$= x_2'$$

$$1011 \ s_{11} = x_1' x_2' \qquad + x_1 x_2' + x_1 x_2 = (x_1 + x_1')x_2'$$
$$+ x_1(x_2' + x_2)$$
$$= x_1 + x_2'$$

$$1100 \ s_{12} = x_1' x_2' + x_1' x_2 \qquad\qquad = x_1'(x_2 + x_2')$$
$$= x_1'$$

$$1101 \ s_{13} = x_1' x_2' + x_1' x_2 \qquad + x_1 x_2 = x_1'(x_2 + x_2')$$
$$+ (x_1' + x_1)x_2$$
$$= x_1' + x_2$$

$$1110 \ s_{14} = x_1' x_2' + x_1' x_2 + x_1 x_2' \qquad = (x_1 + x_1')x_2'$$
$$+ x_1'(x_2 + x_2')$$
$$= x_1' + x_2'$$

$$1111 \ s_{15} = x_1' x_2' + x_1' x_2 + x_1 x_2' + x_1 x_2 = 1$$

switching function, taking into consideration that a product of two factors assumes the value 1 exactly once. Thus, for example,

$$xy = 1 \quad \text{only if } x = 1 \text{ and } y = 1,$$
$$xy' = 1 \quad \text{only if } x = 1 \text{ and } y = 0.$$

With two variables, there are four such products, namely $x_1 x_2$, $x_1' x_2$, $x_1 x_2'$, $x_1' x_2'$. We use these products to describe those positions in the switching function table in which a 1 occurs.

The sixteen functions are pairwise complementary; it follows, as a consequence of the way in which the indices were selected, that

$$s_j' = s_{15-j}, \quad j = 0, 1, \ldots, 15.$$

We see from this enumeration that every bivalent function in the variables x_1 and x_2 can be written in the form

$$s_j = \varepsilon_1 x_1' x_2' + \varepsilon_2 x_1' x_2 + \varepsilon_3 x_1 x_2' + \varepsilon_4 x_1 x_2$$

with

$$\varepsilon_i = \begin{cases} 0 \\ 1 \end{cases}.$$

The binary index j of our switching function can be obtained from the quadruple $(\varepsilon_1, \varepsilon_2, \varepsilon_3, \varepsilon_4)$ by regarding the four values as the digits of a binary number. Thus, for example, the quadruple $(0, 1, 1, 0)$ is associated with the binary index $0110 = 6$, i.e.

$$x_1' x_2 + x_1 x_2' = s_6.$$

In the representation of a switching function s_j as the sum (disjunction) of dual products (complete conjunctions), which we obtain directly from the value table, every summand indicates a position in which s_j assumes the value 1. This is called the *disjunctive normal form* of the switching function. Amongst the many algebraically equivalent representations of a certain switching function s_j, the disjunctive normal form is of especial interest. Because of the duality principle of Boolean algebra, another form of the switching function is also noteworthy; we shall encounter this in Section 5.6.

Problem 78 Let F_2 be the number of switching functions in two variables. Show that the system $[F_2, +, \cdot]$ is a Boolean lattice.

Problem 79 What are the atomic elements of the lattice of Problem 78?

Problem 80 Draw the Hasse diagram of the lattice of Problem 78.

5.5 THE LOGICAL n–1 POLE

The logical n–1 pole is a 2-terminal circuit in which the current can be controlled by n switches; it has n inputs and one output (Figure 67).

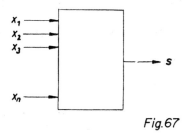

Fig.67

Since every variable x_i can take two values, there are 2^n input constellations (switch positions), and the complete value table of the associated switching function has 2^n lines (see table on p. 150 which has 2^2 lines). Again each input constellation can be associated with the functional value 0 or 1, and so the number of possible switching functions in n variables (or a logical n–1 pole) is equal to the number of 2^n samples, with repetitions, of a 2-set, i.e.

$$\sigma_n = 2^{\left(2^n\right)}.$$

For $n = 3$, there are already $\sigma_3 = 2^8 = 256$ possibilities. Every function may again be characterized by the positions in the value table at which it assumes the value 1. If we note that a product of three factors has the value 1 if, and only if, all its factors are 1, then the following representation for the switching function in three variables is an immediate consequence:

$$s(x_1, x_2, x_3)$$
$$= \varepsilon_1\, x_1'\, x_2'\, x_3' + \varepsilon_2\, x_1'\, x_2'\, x_3 + \varepsilon_3\, x_1'\, x_2\, x_3' + \varepsilon_4\, x_1'\, x_2\, x_3$$
$$+ \varepsilon_5\, x_1\, x_2'\, x_3' + \varepsilon_6\, x_1\, x_2'\, x_3 + \varepsilon_7\, x_1\, x_2\, x_3' + \varepsilon_8\, x_1\, x_2\, x_3,$$

with

$$\varepsilon_i = \begin{cases} 0 \\ 1 \end{cases}.$$

There are $2^3 = 8$ different triple products, i.e. complete conjunctions, in the three variables.

Example (A Binary Adder with transfer.) Design a circuit which will allow one to perform additions in the binary system.

The following additions are, in fact, the only ones we have to consider:

$$0+0 = 0,$$
$$0+1 = 1,$$
$$1+0 = 1,$$
$$1+1 = 10, \text{ i.e. 0 in the corresponding}$$
$$\text{place and carry 1.}$$

Our circuit may be shown diagrammatically as in Figure 68.

The problem leads us to a logical 3–2 pole, which can be directly divided into two logical 3–1 poles. These are characterized by the two switching functions, $s(x_1, x_2, x_3)$ and

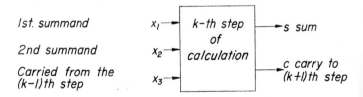

Fig. 68

$c(x_1, x_2, x_3)$, for which we can immediately write down the value tables.

x_1	x_2	x_3	s	c
0	0	0	0	0
0	0	1	1	0
0	1	0	1	0
0	1	1	0	1
1	0	0	1	0
1	0	1	0	1
1	1	0	0	1
1	1	1	1	1

From this, we obtain the two disjunctive normal forms:

$$s(x_1, x_2, x_3) = x_1' x_2' x_3 + x_1' x_2 x_3' + x_1 x_2' x_3' + x_1 x_2 x_3,$$
$$c(x_1, x_2, x_3) = x_1' x_2 x_3 + x_1 x_2' x_3 + x_1 x_2 x_3' + x_1 x_2 x_3.$$

Every term of the switching functions is associated with a certain complete conjunction. The two switching functions can be transformed as follows:

$$s(x_1, x_2, x_3) = x_3' (x_1' x_2 + x_1 x_2') + x_3 (x_1' x_2' + x_1 x_2),$$
$$c(x_1, x_2, x_3) = x_3 (x_1 x_2' + x_1' x_2) + x_1 x_2 \underbrace{(x_3' + x_3)}_{1}$$
$$= x_3 (x_1 x_2' + x_1' x_2) + x_1 x_2.$$

The reader is reminded how the terms in the brackets can be realized by means of transfer contacts. The use of these leads us to the relay circuit shown in Figure 69.

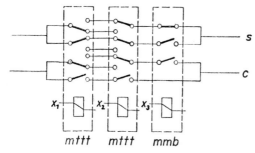

mttt   mttt   mmb   Fig. 69

5.6   THE DISJUNCTIVE AND CONJUNCTIVE NORMAL
FORMS OF A SWITCHING FUNCTION

The behaviour of a logical n–1 pole can be completely described by a switching function and, as indicated by the example in Section 5.5, a switching function can be represented algebraically in several ways. We have already met one special form, the disjunctive normal form, in the case of two and three variables. We shall now introduce normal forms for switching functions with n variables.

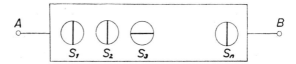

*The path A—B can be controlled
by the n switches $S_1, S_2, \ldots, S_n$*

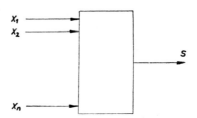

*Symbolic representation
of a logical n—l pole*

Fig. 70

The logical n–1 pole describes a switching circuit, in which the flow of current between two points A and B is governed by n multiple switches. Each switch S_i has two positions; these are described by the variables x_i, which can have the values 0 or 1. The number of different switch positions in our logical n–1 pole is 2^n; a certain constellation can be represented mathematically by the n-tuple $(x_1, x_2, \ldots, x_n)$.

Example   Switch: $S_1\, S_2\, S_3\, S_4 \ldots S_k\, S_{k+1} \ldots S_n$
$$1 \quad 1 \quad 0 \quad 1 \quad \ldots 0 \quad 1 \quad \ldots 1$$

This switch constellation can be associated in an obvious manner with the binary number

$$\mu = 1101 \ldots 01 \ldots 1,$$

so that the value table of the switching function can again be arranged unambiguously. The index μ runs from 0 to 2^n-1.

In addition, we consider the complete conjunctions in the n variables $x_1, x_2, \ldots, x_n$. These are the products with n factors in which every variable occurs exactly once, either directly or in negated form, and it is easily seen that there are 2^n of them.

The set of all switch constellations of the logical n–1 pole and the set of complete conjunctions in n variables have the same order. We can, therefore, define a mapping of one set onto the other by associating a switch constellation of the logical n–1 pole with that complete conjunction formed by replacing the i-th digit in the binary number corresponding to the constellation by x_i if the digit is 1 and by x_i' if the digit is 0 (here we order the digits from *left* to *right*). Thus, the constellation in the above example would be mapped onto the complete conjunction

$$k_\mu = x_1\, x_2\, x_3'\, x_4 \ldots x_k'\, x_{k+1} \ldots x_n.$$

In this way we have obtained a natural ordering for the complete conjunctions: $k_0, k_1, k_2, \ldots, k_{2^n-1}$.

If we now add all those complete conjunctions which correspond to switch positions allowing current to flow between the points A and B, we have the following important representation of the switching function:

$$s(x_1, x_2, \ldots, x_n) = \sum_{\mu=0}^{2^n-1} \varepsilon_\mu k_\mu \text{ with } \varepsilon_\mu = \begin{cases} 0 \\ 1 \end{cases} \in S.$$

This is the disjunctive normal form of the switching function (standard sum); s is here expressed as a disjunction of full conjunctions.

Example   Find the disjunctive normal form of the switching function given by the following value table:

x_1	x_2	x_3	Binary index	s
0	0	0	$000 = 0$	0
0	0	1	$001 = 1$	1
0	1	0	$010 = 2$	1
0	1	1	$011 = 3$	0
1	0	0	$100 = 4$	1
1	0	1	$101 = 5$	1
1	1	0	$110 = 6$	1
1	1	1	$111 = 7$	0

From the table it follows that the disjunctive normal form is

$$\begin{aligned}
s(x_1, x_2, x_3) &= k_1 + k_2 + k_4 + k_5 + k_6 \\
&= x_1' x_2' x_3 + x_1' x_2 x_3' + x_1 x_2' x_3' \\
&\quad + x_1 x_2' x_3 + x_1 x_2 x_3'.
\end{aligned}$$

Figure 71 shows the corresponding realization of this logical 3–1 pole. The circuit contains $3.5 = 15$ active contacts. Note: To every disjunctive normal form in n variables, there corresponds a realization formed from ρ branches in parallel (where ρ is the number of complete conjunctions occurring in s), each branch having n contacts in series.

In this example, the switching function can be considerably simplified. It is found immediately that

$$\begin{aligned}
s(x_1,& x_2, x_3) \\
&= x_2' x_3 x_1' + x_2' x_3 x_1 + x_3' x_1' x_2 + x_3' x_1 x_2' + x_3' x_1 x_2 \\
&= x_2' x_3 (x_1' + x_1) + x_3' (x_1' x_2 + x_1 x_2' + x_1 x_2) \\
&= x_2' x_3 + x_3' [x_1 (x_2 + x_2') + x_1' x_2] \\
&= x_2' x_3 + x_3' (x_1 + x_1' x_2).
\end{aligned}$$

The bracket in the last result may be further simplified, using the first distributive law:

$$x_1 + x_1' x_2 = (x_1 + x_1')(x_1 + x_2) = x_1 + x_2.$$

We have finally:

$$s(x_1, x_2, x_3) = x_2' x_3 + x_3' (x_1 + x_2).$$

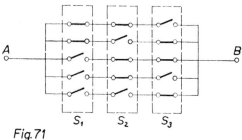

Fig. 71

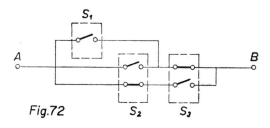

Fig. 72

This representation leads us to the realization shown in Figure 72, which uses only five active contacts.

If the function $s(x_1, x_2, \ldots, x_n)$ is negated, we obtain the corresponding complementary function; this has the value 1 when s has the value 0, and vice versa.

We now introduce a binary index for switching functions in n variables by associating a binary number with the coefficients $(\varepsilon_0, \varepsilon_1, \varepsilon_2, \varepsilon_3, \ldots, \varepsilon_{2^n-1})$. In the last example we found

$$s(x_1, x_2, x_3) = k_1 + k_2 + k_4 + k_5 + k_6,$$

i.e.

$$(\varepsilon_0, \varepsilon_1, \varepsilon_2, \varepsilon_3, \varepsilon_4, \varepsilon_5, \varepsilon_6, \varepsilon_7) = (0, 1, 1, 0, 1, 1, 1, 0).$$

The above switching function has therefore got the binary index

$$v = 01101110 = 110_{10}.$$

With n variables, the index v runs from 0 to $m = 2^{2^n-1}$.

It is easily seen that for any v, we have

$$s'_v = s_{m-v}.$$

We shall now negate a given function $s(x_1, x_2, \ldots, x_n)$, the disjunctive normal form of which is known:

$$s(x_1, x_2, \ldots, x_n) = \sum_{\mu=0}^{2^n-1} \varepsilon_\mu k_\mu.$$

To do this, we use de Morgan's general theorem:

$$(x_1 + x_2 + \ldots + x_n)' = x'_1 \cdot x'_2 \cdot \ldots \cdot x'_n,$$
$$(x_1 \cdot x_2 \cdot \ldots \cdot x_n)' = x'_1 + x'_2 + \ldots + x'_n.*$$

These relations were previously mentioned in Section 2.3 for the case $n = 2$. We conclude, therefore, that

$$s'(x_1, x_2, \ldots, x_n) = \left(\sum_{\mu=0}^{2^n-1} \varepsilon_\mu k_\mu \right)' = \prod_{\mu=0}^{2^n-1} (\varepsilon_\mu k_\mu)'$$
$$= \prod_{\mu=0}^{2^n-1} (\varepsilon'_\mu + k'_\mu).$$

In order more fully to understand the negation of a complete conjunction, we shall first consider the example,

$$k_\mu = x_1 x_2 x'_3 x_4 \ldots x_k x'_{k+1} \ldots x_n.$$

It follows from de Morgan's second rule that

$$k'_\mu = x'_1 + x'_2 + x_3 + x'_4 + \ldots + x'_k + x_{k+1} + \ldots + x'_n = d_\mu,$$

say. d_μ is an n-member sum in which every variable occurs exactly once either directly or negated. This is called a complete disjunction. If we associate the resulting complete disjunction with the binary index

$$\mu' = 0010 \ldots 01 \ldots 0,$$

then it is obvious that

$$\mu + \mu' = 1111 \ldots 11 \ldots 1 = 2^n - 1.$$

*Cf. Problem 27.

From this it follows that the negation of a complete conjunction is given by

$$k'_\mu = d_{2^n-1-\mu}.$$

Thus we have:

$$s'(x_1, x_2, \ldots, x_n) = \prod_{\mu=0}^{2^n-1} (\varepsilon'_\mu + k'_\mu) = \prod_{\mu=0}^{2^n-1} (\varepsilon'_\mu + d'_{2^n-1-\mu}).$$

s' appears as the product (conjunction) of complete disjunctions. This is called the conjunctive normal form of the corresponding switching function. In view of the duality principle of Boolean algebra, this second important representation of a switching function could have been anticipated.

Our considerations led us first to the conjunctive normal form of the function s'; this is the function with the value distribution $(\varepsilon'_0, \varepsilon'_1, \varepsilon'_2, \ldots, \varepsilon'_{2^n-1})$. Assuming instead the value distribution $(\varepsilon_0, \varepsilon_1, \varepsilon_2, \ldots, \varepsilon_{2^n-1})$, we have immediately the conjunctive normal form of the original function s, i.e.,

$$s(x_1, x_2, \ldots, x_n) = \prod_{\mu=0}^{2^n-1} (\varepsilon_\mu + d_{2^n-1-\mu}).$$

It should be noted that all brackets in which $\varepsilon_\mu = 1$ have the conductance 1, and so can be omitted from the product. The zero positions of the switching functions determine the conjunctive normal form since they are associated with the brackets of importance.

We shall now consider these results with reference to our earlier example. In that, the switching function s was given by

$$\varepsilon_1 = \varepsilon_2 = \varepsilon_4 = \varepsilon_5 = \varepsilon_6 = 1 \text{ or } \varepsilon_0 = \varepsilon_3 = \varepsilon_7 = 0.$$

Accordingly, we study the following complete disjunctions:

$$\varepsilon_0 \to d_{7-0} = d_7 = x_1 + x_2 + x_3,$$
$$\varepsilon_3 \to d_{7-3} = d_4 = x_1 + x'_2 + x'_3,$$
$$\varepsilon_7 \to d_{7-7} = d_0 = x'_1 + x'_2 + x'_3.$$

Hence, the conjunctive normal form is

$$s(x_1, x_2, x_3) = (x_1 + x_2 + x_3)(x_1 + x'_2 + x'_3)(x'_1 + x'_2 + x'_3).$$

This corresponds to the realization shown in Figure 73. Note

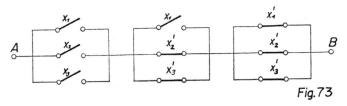

Fig.73

the structure of this circuit: it is formed by branches, with three parallel switches in each, in series.

In our investigations, the disjunctive normal form of the switching function has been emphasized. Circuits resulting from this are generally more obvious. Naturally, the conjunctive normal form may also be obtained directly, instead of by transformation of the disjunctive normal form. In this

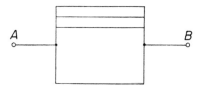

Disjunctive normal form
p parallel branches of n
contacts. This realization requires
np contacts

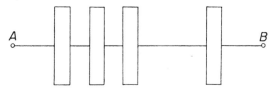

Conjunctive normal form
$2^n - p$ branches, each with n contacts,
in series. This realization requires
$n(2^n - p)$ contacts

                  Fig.74

case, the zero values of the switching function form the starting point, and note must be taken that a complete disjunction is zero only when all its summands are zero. We obtain the conjunctive normal form of a switching function by multiplying together all the complete disjunctions corresponding to zero values of s.

It is easy to calculate the number of active contacts needed for circuits corresponding to either of the normal forms of the switching function (see Figure 74). As above, we let ρ be the number of unit values of the switching function under consideration.

In practice, the disjunctive normal form is the more important.

5.7 EXAMPLES IN SWITCHING ALGEBRA

Problem 81 The two-switch problem. Design a circuit connecting two switches and a light bulb in such a way that the light can be turned on or off from either switch.

The positions of the switches s_1, s_2 are determined by the two variables x_1 and x_2 respectively. The switching function $f(x_1, x_2)$ has the following value table:

x_1	x_2	$f(x_1, x_2)$
0	0	0
0	1	1
1	0	1
1	1	0

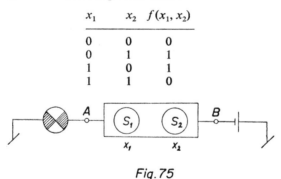

Fig. 75

The light should be turned on when exactly one switch is closed. From the value table we see immediately that the disjunctive normal form is

$$f(x_1, x_2) = x_1' x_2 + x_1 x_2'.$$

Similarly we obtain the conjunctive normal form:

$$f(x_1, x_2) = (x_1' + x_2')(x_1 + x_2).$$

The first normal form corresponds to the realization in Figure 76, which may be further simplified by the use of transfer contacts.

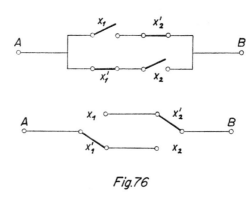

Fig.76

The term $x_1' x_2 + x_1 x_2'$ is symmetrical in x_1 and x_2; the present circuit is characterized by a symmetric switching function. Since this function occurs very frequently in applications, it is denoted by a special symbol:

$$x_1' x_2 + x_1 x_2' = x_1 / x_2 {}^*$$

It is then easy to check that:

$$x_1 / x_2 = x_2 / x_1,$$
$$x_1' / x_2 = x_1' x_2' + x_1 x_2 = x_1 / x_2',$$
$$(x_1 / x_2)' = x_1' / x_2,$$

$$(x_1 / x_2) / x_3 = x_1 / (x_2 / x_3)$$
$$= x_1 x_2' x_3' + x_1' x_2 x_3' + x_1' x_2' x_3 + x_1 x_2 x_3.$$

This is again a symmetric function; it is written as $x_1 / x_2 / x_3$.

*An alternative notation used in logic is $x_1 \pm x_2$. The symbol $\pm$ is called *exclusive disjunction*.

The corresponding problem for three switches leads to the switching function

$$f(x_1, x_2, x_3) = x_1 x_2' x_3' + x_1' x_2 x_3' + x_1' x_2' x_3 + x_1 x_2 x_3$$
$$= x_1 / x_2 / x_3$$
$$= (x_1 / x_2) x_3' + (x_1 / x_2)' x_3.$$

The circuit of Figure 77 is a realization of this last representation. This may be immediately transformed into the circuit of Figure 78.

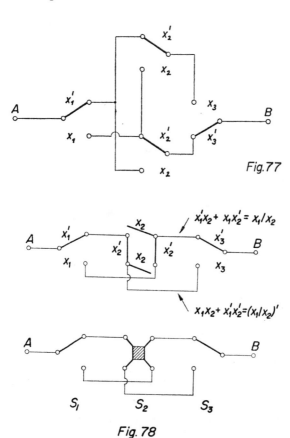

Fig. 77

Fig. 78

The switch S_2 is called a *cross switch*. Note the conductance of the two branches leading into the switch S_2. If a further cross switch is provided instead of S_3 (transfer contact), then the two output terminals will have the conductances shown in Figure 79.

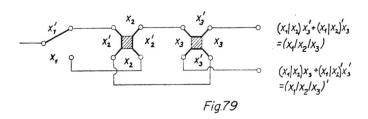

Fig.79

This enables us to solve the general problem for n switches, which arises, for example, where a staircase lighting installation is to be operated from n different switches.

To obtain the switching function for, say, $n = 5$, we must note that the light must be on if, and only if, the associated x_i have the value 1 for 1, 3 or 5 switches. The switching function has, therefore

$$\binom{5}{1} + \binom{5}{3} + \binom{5}{5} = 16 \text{ terms.}$$

It reads:

$f(x_1, x_2, x_3, x_4, x_5)$
$= x_1 x_2' x_3' x_4' x_5' + x_1' x_2 x_3' x_4' x_5' + x_1' x_2' x_3 x_4' x_5' + x_1' x_2' x_3' x_4 x_5'$
$+ x_1' x_2' x_3' x_4' x_5 + x_1 x_2 x_3 x_4' x_5' + x_1 x_2 x_3' x_4 x_5' + x_1 x_2' x_3 x_4 x_5'$
$+ x_1' x_2 x_3 x_4 x_5' + x_1 x_2 x_3' x_4' x_5 + x_1 x_2' x_3 x_4' x_5 + x_1' x_2 x_3 x_4' x_5$
$+ x_1 x_2' x_3' x_4 x_5 + x_1' x_2 x_3' x_4 x_5 + x_1' x_2' x_3 x_4 x_5 + x_1 x_2 x_3 x_4 x_5.$

and, after several transformations,

$$f(x_1, x_2, x_3, x_4, x_5) = (x_1 / x_2 / x_3)(x_4 / x_5)' + (x_1 / x_2 / x_3)'(x_4 / x_5).$$

This last representation is easily realizable, if we make use of the results established earlier (see Figure 79). This leads to the circuit shown in Figure 80.

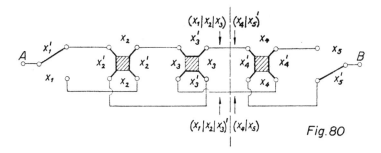

Fig. 80

Problem 82 Describe the function

$$f(A_1, A_2) = A_1 / A_2 = (A_1' \cap A_2) \cup (A_1 \cap A_2')$$

on a finite power set lattice, and draw the corresponding Venn diagram. The set combination A_1/A_2 is sometimes called the *symmetric difference* between A_1 and A_2 (see Figure 33).

Problem 83 Draw a Venn diagram to illustrate the function

$$f(A_1, A_2, A_3) = A_1 / A_2 / A_3$$

on a finite power set lattice.

Problem 84 Let

$$f(x_1, x_2, \ldots, x_n) = \sigma_n$$

be the switching function for the *n*-switch problem. Show that:
  (a) σ_n is a symmetric function (i.e., every permutation of the variables leaves σ_n unaltered);
  (b) the disjunctive normal form for σ_n consists of the complete conjunctions of odd orders (see Problems 45 and 47).

Problem 85 Show that the function σ_n satisfies the recurrence relation

$$\sigma_{n+1} = \sigma_n x'_{n+1} + \sigma_n' x_{n+1} = \sigma_n / x_{n+1}.$$

Problem 86 Prove by induction that the *n*-switch problem can be solved by means of a 2-terminal circuit consisting of

$n-2$ cross switches and two transfer contacts, at the two ends of the circuit (see also Figure 80).

Hint: Remove the right-hand transfer contact in the circuit for the n-switch problem and replace it, as in Figure 80, by a suitable combination of a cross switch and a transfer contact so that the new circuit solves the $(n+1)$–switch problem.

Problem 87 Let F_k be the set of all switching functions in k variables $x_1, x_2, \ldots, x_k$. Show that the system $[F_k, +, \cdot]$ is a Boolean lattice. Find $n(F_k)$.

Problem 88 Let S_k be the set of all symmetric switching functions in k variables. Show that the system $[S_k, +, \cdot]$ is a Boolean lattice. Find $n(S_k)$.

Problem 89 Find the atomic elements of the two lattices

$$[F_k, +, \cdot] \text{ and } [S_k, +, \cdot].$$

Problem 90 Draw the Hasse diagrams of the lattices

$$[F_k, +, \cdot] \text{ and } [S_k, +, \cdot].$$

Problem 91 A control device is to be designed so that a lamp will light when exactly two of three machines are in operation. Assume that a machine when running gives the conductance 1, and hence find the switching function required.

The value table of the switching function is as follows:

x_1	x_2	x_3	$f(x_1, x_2, x_3)$
0	0	0	0
0	0	1	0
0	1	0	0
0	1	1	1
1	0	0	0
1	0	1	1
1	1	0	1
1	1	1	0

The position of the '1's in the right-hand column gives us the disjunctive normal form:

$$f(x_1, x_2, x_3) = x_1' x_2 x_3 + x_1 x_2' x_3 + x_1 x_2 x_3'$$
$$= x_1 (x_2 / x_3) + x_3 (x_1 / x_2).$$

The latter representation is obtained by noting that every summand can be repeated as often as desired.

Problem 92 On an assembly line, there are n processing stations B_i. One does not want the station B_i to operate when the next station B_{i+1} is inoperative. Design a circuit to indicate, by means of a warning lamp, if the way ahead is not clear at some point. (We assume that the station B_i when operating gives the conductance $x_i = 1$ as information.)

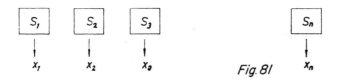

Fig. 81

The prohibited states are characterized by at least one 0 following a 1 in the sequence of the n conductances x_i. Since n is indeterminate, we cannot write down the complete value table of the switching function, and must make do with the following section:

x_1	x_2	x_3	x_4	x_n	s	
1	1	1	1	1	0	
0	1	1	1	1	0	permitted
0	0	1	1	1	0	states
0	0	0	1	1	0	
.	.	.	.	.	.	
.	.	.	.	.	.	
0	0	1	0		1	
0	1	0	1		1	prohibited
1	1	0	1		1	states

The switching function is zero if, and only if, in the sequence of the x_i there are k '0's followed by $n-k$ '1's. It therefore takes the value zero exactly $n+1$ times. Since, in this case we are particularly interested in the zero values, we start with the conjunctive normal form. This reads:

$$s(x_1, x_2, \ldots, x_n)$$
$$= (x'_1 + x'_2 + x'_3 + \ldots + x'_n)(x_1 + x'_2 + x'_3 + \ldots + x'_n) \ldots$$
$$\ldots (x_1 + x_2 + x_3 + \ldots + x_n).$$

In order to avoid having to make use of the somewhat difficult second distributive law, we use the complementary function:

$$s' = x_1 x_2 x_3 \ldots x_n + x'_1 x_2 x_3 \ldots x_n + x'_1 x'_2 x_3 \ldots x_n + \ldots$$
$$\ldots + x'_1 x'_2 x'_3 \ldots x'_n.$$

Again we use the fact that every term can be repeated as often as desired. The combination of the first and second terms gives

$$x_1 x_2 x_3 \ldots x_n + x'_1 x_2 x_3 \ldots x_n = x_2 x_3 \ldots x_n.$$

The sum of the second and third terms gives

$$x'_1 x_2 x_3 \ldots x_n + x'_1 x'_2 x_3 \ldots x_n = x'_1 x_3 \ldots x_n.$$

Hence, by summing successive pairs of terms, we obtain

$$s' = x_2 x_3 x_4 \ldots x_n + x'_1 x_3 x_4 \ldots x_n + x'_1 x'_2 x_4 \ldots x_n + \ldots$$
$$\ldots + x'_1 x'_2 x'_3 \ldots x'_{n-1}$$
$$= (x'_1 + x_2)(x'_2 + x_3)(x'_3 + x_4) \ldots (x'_{n-1} + x_n).$$

If one multiplies out the brackets one obtains the terms in the first line and, in addition, a series of terms containing products of the type $x_k x'_k$ which are all equal to zero. Finally, by taking complements, we obtain the required switching function:

$$s = x_1 x'_2 + x_2 x'_3 + x_3 x'_4 + \ldots + x_{n-1} x'_n.$$

5.8 THE SYMBOLIC REPRESENTATION OF SWITCHING FUNCTIONS

The switching function has provided us with an adequate mathematical aid for describing the electrical behaviour of 2-terminal circuits. An essential structural element in such circuits is the multiple switch or the electro-magnetic relay.

Circuits in which only two states are of interest in each branch*
are called digital circuits, of which 2-terminal circuits are a
particular example. These circuits can be realized in other
ways (electron tubes, transistors, magnetic cores), and it is
possible for the digital circuits to include relay coils.

The electrical realization of the switching functions described
so far was based entirely on the use of relays. This was sug-
gested by the construction of our switching algebra.

In engineering, there is a tendency to construct digital
circuits from a few special types of logical n–1 poles. This is
possible, for example, by using the following units:

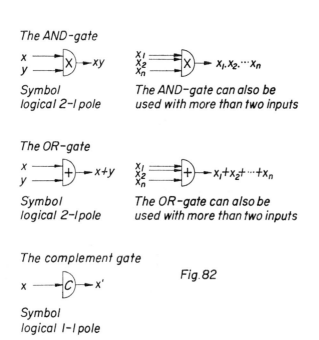

The AND-gate

Symbol
logical 2-1 pole

The AND-gate can also be
used with more than two inputs

The OR-gate

Symbol
logical 2-1 pole

The OR-gate can also be
used with more than two inputs

The complement gate

Fig.82

Symbol
logical 1-1 pole

---

*Possible pairs of states are, for example, voltage and no-voltage, voltage
of 1V and voltage of 10V.

Problem 93   Realize the three units by means of relays.

In principle, two of these units would be sufficient, since the relation

$$xy = (x'+y')',$$

enables us to replace the AND-gate by a combination of the other two units. Figure 83(a) shows how this can be done.

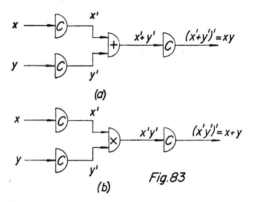

(a)

(b)   *Fig.83*

By the duality principle it follows that, by means of the dual relation

$$x+y = (x'y')',$$

one can avoid the use of the OR-gate. The circuit which will do this is shown in Figure 83(b).

Both circuits have a certain practical importance. For, in circuits involving valves, depending upon the voltages in the input circuits, AND-gates must sometimes by replaced by OR-gates, or vice versa.

The principle of constructing networks by means of logical units leads simultaneously to a method for symbolizing switching functions, in which the special technique of realization (relays, valves, transistors) is eliminated completely.

As a first application of the symbolic notation, Figure 84 shows the two distributive laws of switching algebra. The figures clearly emphasize the duality of the laws.

We shall now use this symbolic notation to describe some of the circuits discussed above. Such a diagram is often referred to as a *logical circuit diagram*.

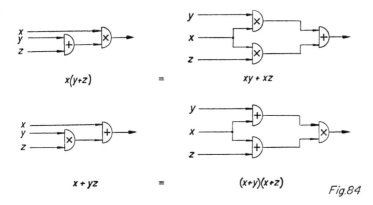

Fig.84

In Problem 91 we obtained the switching function

$$f(x_1, x_2, x_3) = x_1' x_2 x_3 + x_1 x_2' x_3 + x_1 x_2 x_3'$$
$$= x_1 (x_2' x_3 + x_2 x_3') + x_3 (x_1' x_2 + x_1 x_2').$$

The last form leads to the logical diagram shown in Figure 85.

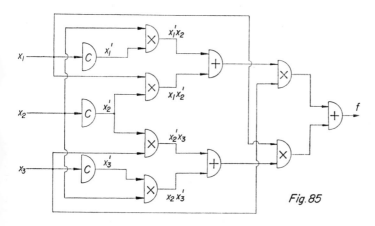

Fig.85

In Problem 92, the switching function for $n = 4$ is

$$s(x_1, x_2, x_3, x_4) = x_1' x_2 + x_2' x_3 + x_3' x_4.$$

The corresponding logical diagram is shown in Figure 86.

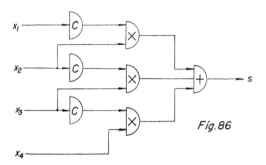

Fig.86

Apart from being independent of the particular technique used, the logical diagram is also much clearer than, say, the corresponding relay diagram.

As a last example, we shall deal with the binary adder. In Section 5.4 we found the following switching functions were required:

$$s(x_1, x_2, x_3) = x_3'(x_1' x_2 + x_1 x_2') + x_3 (x_1' x_2' + x_1 x_2),$$
$$c(x_1, x_2, x_3) = x_1 x_2 + x_3 (x_1' x_2 + x_1 x_2').$$

Before drawing the logical diagram, we shall transform the switching functions s and c. We note first that both terms in brackets in the function s are complementary, since, according to de Morgan's laws,

$$(x_1' x_2' + x_1 x_2)' = (x_1' x_2')'(x_1 x_2)' - (x_1 + x_2)(x_1' + x_2')$$
$$= x_1' x_2 + x_1 x_2'.$$

Thus, s can be written as follows:

$$s = x_3'(x_1' x_2 + x_1 x_2') + x_3 (x_1' x_2 + x_1 x_2')'$$
$$= (x_1' x_2 + x_1 x_2' + x_3)((x_1' x_2 + x_1 x_2')' + x_3').$$

To obtain a simplified form for c, we use the first distributive law:

$$x_2 + x_3 x_2' = (x_2 + x_3)(x_2 + x_2') = x_2 + x_3,$$
$$x_1 + x_3 x_1' = (x_1 + x_3)(x_1 + x_1') = x_1 + x_3.$$

Making use of this result, we obtain

$$c = x_1 x_2 + x_3 (x_1 + x_2).$$

We now draw the diagrams for s and c together, and so obtain the logical diagram for the binary adder shown in Figure 87.

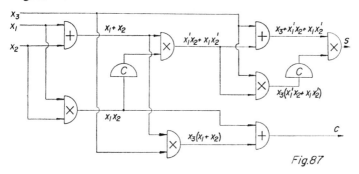

Fig.87

5.9 DIGITAL CIRCUITS WITH SEQUENTIAL BEHAVIOUR

Our introduction to switching algebra was based upon one particular technical construction—we always thought in terms of mechanical switches (contact networks). In the construction of digital circuits the electromagnetic relay is by far the most versatile unit. This is because of certain specific properties of relays:

(a) A single control circuit (coil) can move several contacts simultaneously.

(b) A relay is the only unit which can simultaneously contain contacts in complementary positions.

(c) In a relay, the control circuit (coil) and the output circuit are electrically completely independent. Although loading of the secondary circuits may occasionally damage the contacts (pitting), it can never affect the power balance of the control circuit.

However, these advantages are balanced by certain drawbacks, principally the comparatively long switching time, this leads to a low switching frequency of, for example, not more than 15 c/s in telecommunication relays. For this reason, relays are used in computers nowadays only for special switching tasks

The following considerations will take us somewhat beyond

switching algebra. We shall deal briefly with a class of relay circuits which demonstrates clearly the versatility of the electromagnetic relay.

Switching algebra is closely linked with the theory of the logical n–1 pole. In this circuit, the output depends on the position of n inputs (switches), so that the same switch position results always in the same output conductance, without regard to the constellations which have meanwhile been set in the circuit. The temporal sequence of different conditions has no effect on the output conductance. The logical n–1 pole is a circuit without sequential behaviour. This state of affairs is reflected in the switching function which describes the electrical behaviour of the logical n–1 pole. A simple example will show that there are other possibilities.

We start with the logical circuit of Figure 88(a). An attempt to introduce the switching function s as an input, leads to the relation $s = x + s$, in which the variable s occurs on both sides of the equals sign. Since in Boolean algebra there are no inverse operations to addition and multiplication, this equation cannot be solved for s. A short investigation shows that we cannot find a switching function to describe this circuit. For, it is clear that $x = 0$ and $s = 0$ are compatible values. However, once $x = 1$, s will be 1 continuously thereafter, even

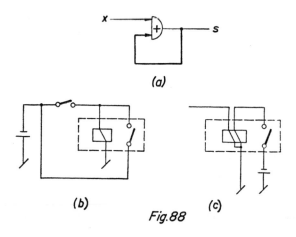

(a)

(b)   (c)

Fig. 88

if x returns to 0. This behaviour is in contradiction to that of the switching functions we have met. We now have a *sequential circuit*. This class of circuits is characterized by so-called *feedback* branches, whereby an output conductance is fed back into the input. In Figure 88(a), the feedback is indicated by solid lines. This circuit has the property of storage (it is a memory circuit). Figures 88(b) and 88(c) show two realizations using relays.

We stress that the range of the logical notation exceeds that of switching functions, for it enables us to represent sequential circuits.

In our first example, we see a circuit which is of paramount importance in the construction of computers, although it will usually be somewhat modified in practice. For example, if the memory stage is to be externally

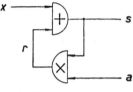

Fig.89

controlled, the circuit must be completed as shown in Figure 89. The stage will remain fixed only if $a = 1$. In this way, the memory can be suppressed or limited in time. The feedback may be described by the switching function $r = as$.

5.9.1 *The pulse memory stage*

We shall now modify the circuit just described so that it also records the end of a pulse. This provides a means of constructing counting and recording circuits. (See Figure 90(a).)

The circuit can only store information when $a = 1$. When x then assumes the value 1 (beginning of the pulse), s also becomes 1 and remains 1, so long as $a = 1$. When x later becomes 0 (end of the pulse), $x's = 1$. The temporal sequence can be represented by means of a so-called *transit time diagram* (Figure 90(b)). Figure 90(c) shows a possible realization using relays; the lower relay is energized at the start of the pulse ($s = 1$), and the upper relay at the end of the pulse ($s = 1$, $s^* = 1$).

5.9.2 *The ring counter*

Pulse counters are important units in computers; however,

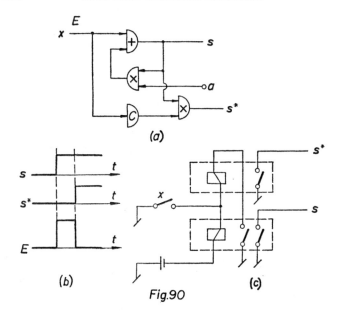

Fig.90

they are also used in other branches of digital control circuitry, for example, telecommunications.

The decade ring counter consists of ten memory stages, coupled in the form of an annulus so that at all times exactly one stage S_j is activated ($s_j = 1$ and $s_j^* = 1$). A pulse arriving at the input of the counter erases S_j and simultaneously activates S_{j+1}.

Figure 91(a) shows a block diagram and Figure 91(b) the logical circuit for three consecutive stages S_{j-1}, S_j and S_{j+1} of a ring counter. The indices are to be thought of modulo 10.

A counter constructed according to this diagram has, however, the great drawback that it will never begin to operate. In order to remedy this, the circuit must be completed so that the first pulse arriving at E always activates a certain stage, e.g. the stage corresponding to the digit 1. If, say, S_{j-1} is this particular stage, then a feedback with the switching function

$$a = (s_0^*)'(s_1^*)'(s_2^*)' \ldots (s_9^*)'$$

is introduced at the point A.

5.9.3 *The flip-flop*

This is a circuit with two stable states, controlled by pulses. It can be easily seen that, in the logical circuit of Figure 92(a), only the two states $u_1 = 0$, $u_2 = 1$ and $u_1 = 1$, $u_2 = 0$ are stable. They can be caused by pulses applied to the inputs E_1 and E_2. If the flip-flop is, for example, in the position $u_1 = 1$, $u_2 = 0$, it will change after a pulse applied at E_2 to $u_1 = 0$,

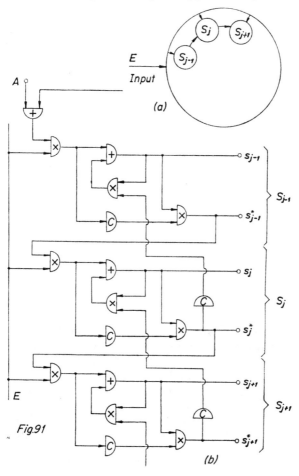

Fig.91

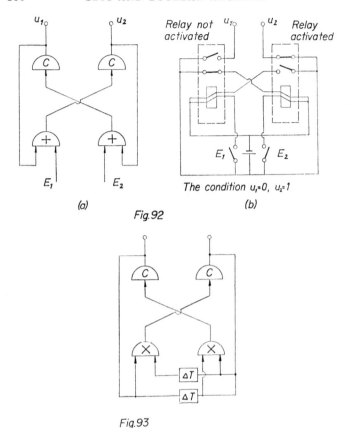

Fig. 92

Fig. 93

$u_2 = 1$. A further pulse at E_2 brings about no change, while a pulse applied at E_1 causes the flip-flop to move back into the first state. Figure 92(b) shows a possible construction of a flip-flop using a two-coil relay. Contrary to the convention we adopted for logical $n-1$ poles, the relay on the right side is shown in the energized state.

By means of two feedbacks with suitable delay members, the flip-flop may be altered into an oscillator; Figure 93 shows the logical circuit of a so-called *multivibrator*. The time delay may be achieved, say, by charging a capacitor.

5.10 GEOMETRICAL REDUCTION AND CLASSIFICATION OF SWITCHING FUNCTIONS

In this last section, we shall show an interesting connection between switching algebra and the symmetry group of the n-dimensional cube. In order to remain within the framework of intuitive geometry, we shall limit ourselves to a complete representation of the conditions for switching functions in three variables. This will be preceded by a brief look at the general case.

With n variables, the number of possible complete conjunctions is 2^n. This is also the number of vertices of an n-dimensional cube. Thus, we can map the complete conjunctions in a one-to-one manner onto the vertices of a cube. Assuming the unit cube is on the axes of a Cartesian system of coordinates, the following mapping suggests itself: the complete conjunction k_μ, is associated with that vertex of the cube whose coordinates correspond to the digits of the binary index μ. For example, for $n = 3$, the complete conjunction $x_1 x_2 x_3'$ has the binary index $110 (= 6)$; thus the mapping is as follows:

$$\text{complete conjunction} \rightarrow \text{cube vertex}$$
$$x_1 x_2 x_3' \qquad P_6 (1, 1, 0).$$

A consequence of this correspondence is that certain problems concerning switching functions can now be related to geometrical problems.

The left part of Figure 94 shows the eight vertices of a cube, marked with their coordinates and binary index. In the

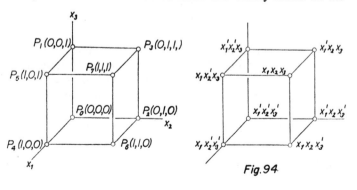

Fig. 94.

right part, these descriptions have been replaced by the corresponding complete conjunctions. By means of this mapping of the complete conjunctions onto the vertices of the three-dimensional cube, we are able to illustrate a switching function in three variables geometrically: we indicate in the drawing those vertices of the cube which are associated with complete conjunctions occurring in the given switching function.

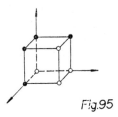

Fig.95

Figure 95 shows, by way of example, the geometrical representation of the function

$$f(x_1, x_2, x_3) = x_1' x_2 x_3 + x_1 x_2' x_3 + x_1 x_2' x_3' + x_1' x_2' x_3.$$

By combining pairs of complete conjunctions this function can be simplified as follows:

$$f(x_1, x_2, x_3) = x_1 x_2' (x_3 + x_3') + x_1' x_3 (x_2 + x_2')$$
$$= x_1 x_2' + x_1' x_3.$$

If one considers the geometrical implications of this, one sees that two complete conjunctions can be combined if they are associated with vertices which form the endpoints of one of the edges of the cube. Generally, the following reduction rule applies:

1. In every sum of two complete conjunctions associated with the endpoints of a cube edge, two factors can be bracketed, and the bracket always has the value 1. Each cube edge can therefore be associated with a product of two variables (or their complements).

In order to carry out this association, it is only necessary to note that two adjacent cube vertices are always associated with complete conjunctions having two factors in common and third factors which are complementary.

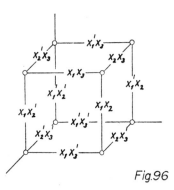

Fig.96

Figure 96 shows the relation between the cube edges and the dual products.

Moreover, it can also be seen that:

2. In each sum of four complete conjunctions, associated with the vertices of any face of the cube, a factor can be bracketed, and the remaining bracket always has the value 1. Each face of the cube can therefore be associated with a variable or its complement. As an example of this second reduction rule:

$$x_1' x_2 x_3 + x_1' x_2' x_3 + x_1' x_2 x_3' + x_1' x_2' x_3'$$
$$= x_1' (x_2 x_3 + x_2' x_3 + x_2 x_3' + x_2' x_3')$$
$$= x_1' (x_2 + x_2')(x_3 + x_3') = x_1'.$$

Obviously the four complete conjunctions associated with the vertices of one face always contain a common factor. After taking out this factor, there remains a term of the form

$$x_i x_k + x_i' x_k + x_i x_k' + x_i' x_k' = (x_i + x_i')(x_k + x_k') \text{ with } i \neq k.$$

The correspondence between complete conjunctions and the cube vertices may therefore be extended: the cube edges can be made to correspond to the dual products and the cube faces to the 'unit' products.

Taking into consideration that every term in any switching function may be repeated several times, simplifications can now be carried out using these two reduction rules, which are based on a geometrical configuration. We give three examples

$$f(x_1, x_2, x_3) = x_1 x_2' x_3 + x_1 x_2 x_3' + x_1' x_2 x_3' + x_1' x_2' x_3$$
$$+ x_1' x_2' x_3'$$
$$= x_2' x_3 + x_1' x_3' + x_2 x_3'.$$
$$g(x_1, x_2, x_3) = x_1 x_2 + x_1 x_2' x_3 = x_1 x_2 + x_1 x_3.$$

By setting $x_1 = 1$ in the last example, we have the function

$$h(x_1, x_2, x_3) = x_2 + x_2' x_3 = (x_2 + x_3)(x_2 + x_2') = x_2 + x_3.$$

The corresponding geometrical configurations are shown on the cubes in Figure 97.

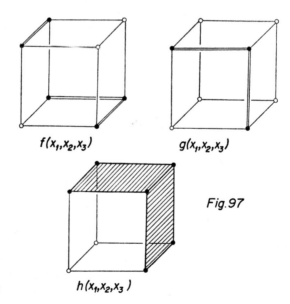

$f(x_1, x_2, x_3)$

$g(x_1, x_2, x_3)$

Fig. 97

$h(x_1, x_2, x_3)$

5.10.1 *A classification of switching functions in three variables*

Our mapping of the complete conjunctions onto the vertices of a cube has further application. We shall now deal briefly with a problem in which a link with group theory comes to light.

Let us consider the set F_n of all switching functions in n variables. Then the order of F_n is $2^{(2^n)}$ (see Problem 87). The following table indicates how rapidly the order of F_n increases with n.

n	Order of F_n
1	4
2	16
3	256
4	65, 536
5	4, 294, 967, 296

We shall now show a classification for F_3, inspired by geometry, which has also some practical uses. This will help us to understand more about the set F_3.

Let G_C be the group of symmetry transformations of the cube. G_C may be obtained by starting from the set S of reflections in a plane which map the cube onto itself. G_C is the set of all finite products of mappings of S. The elements of S are three reflections in the central planes and six reflections in the diagonal planes of the cube. Figure 98 shows the central plane α and the diagonal plane β.

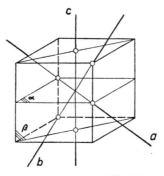

Fig. 98

Listing the elements of G_C we obtain:

(a) *Direct Isometries*

Identity	1
Half-turns about the mediators of pairs of opposite edges (e.g. axis a)	6
120° and 240° rotations about the cube diagonals (e.g. axis b)	8
Rotations about lines joining the centres of opposite faces through 90°, 180° and 270° (e.g. axis c)	9

Number of rotations	24

These 24 rotations form the subgroup $D \subset G_C$. We mention that each rotation can be obtained as the product of two reflections in a plane.

(b) *Opposite Isometries*

Central symmetry across the cube centre	1
Symmetries in a plane	9
Rotational symmetries* of order 3	8
Rotational symmetries of order 4	6

	24

The group G_C has the order 48; D is the subgroup with index 2**. Every opposite isometry is either a plane reflection or the product of three plane reflections.

We shall now consider the geometrical representation of a switching function in three variables; it consists of several marked vertices on a cube. Starting with this representation, we introduce an equivalence relation on the set F_3.

Definition Two switching functions are said to be equivalent if the geometrical representation of the second is the image of the representation of the first under one of the transformations which belong to G_C.

---

*A rotational symmetry is a combination of a rotation and a reflection in a plane perpendicular to the axis of rotation.

**The index of a subgroup is the ratio of the order of the group containing it to the order of the subgroup.

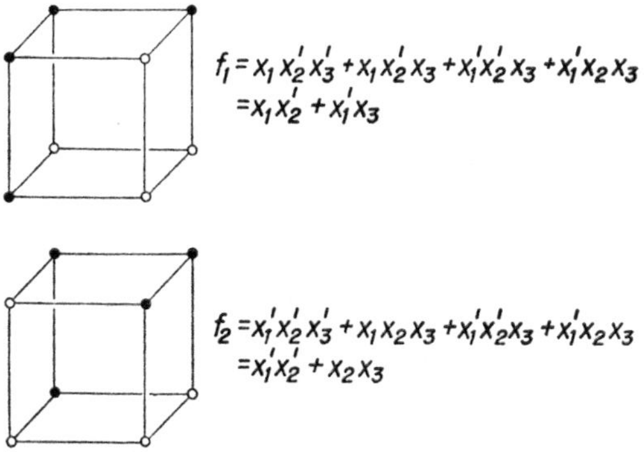

$f_1 = x_1 x_2' x_3' + x_1 x_2' x_3 + x_1' x_2' x_3 + x_1' x_2 x_3$

$\quad = x_1 x_2' + x_1' x_3$

$f_2 = x_1' x_2' x_3' + x_1 x_2 x_3 + x_1' x_2' x_3 + x_1' x_2 x_3$

$\quad = x_1' x_2' + x_2 x_3$

Fig. 99

Hence, for example, the two switching functions in Figure 99 are in the same equivalence class.

We shall now investigate the relevance of this equivalence for the switching functions. First, it is obvious that the disjunctive normal forms of equivalent functions contain the same number of complete conjunctions. It is, however, clear that a certain equivalence class cannot be characterized only by the number of complete conjunctions. In order to obtain further information, we shall again use an example. Let us consider a particular element of G_C, a $120°$ rotation about the axis d, which we shall denote by Δ.

The face of the cube which is associated with x_1 is mapped by Δ onto the face associated with x_2. Since under any isometry opposite faces stay opposite, it follows that

$$\text{if } x_1 \rightarrow x_2, \text{ then } x_1' \rightarrow x_2'.$$

The other images of the cube faces under Δ are given by:

$$x_2 \rightarrow x_3' \quad \text{and} \quad x_2' \rightarrow x_3,$$
$$x_3 \rightarrow x_1' \quad \text{and} \quad x_3' \rightarrow x_1.$$

The mapping Δ can therefore be described as follows:

$$\Delta \begin{cases} x_1 \rightarrow x_2 \\ x_2 \rightarrow x_3' \\ x_3 \rightarrow x_1'. \end{cases}$$

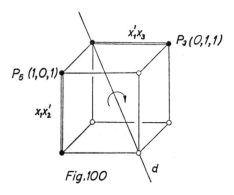

Fig.100

For example, the complete conjunction $x_1 x_2' x_3$ is transformed into the complete conjunction $x_2 x_3 x_1' = x_1' x_2 x_3$. In geometrical language (Figure 100), this means that Δ maps the vertex $P_5(1, 0, 1)$ onto the vertex $P_3(0, 1, 1)$.

Every mapping $\theta \in G_C$ is equivalent to a substitution of the form:

$$\left.\begin{array}{l} x_1 \rightarrow x_i' \\ x_2 \rightarrow x_j \\ x_3 \rightarrow x_k' \end{array}\right\}$$ i, j, k, all differ. The number of complements (negations) appearing on the right-hand side can vary between none and three.

The variables are permutated and possibly negated. As can be easily seen, there are, in fact, $2^3.3! = 48$ such substitutions; $3!$ representing the permutations, and 2^3 the negations.

Let us now suppose we are given a circuit corresponding to the function $f(x_1, x_2, x_3)$. The image of f resulting from the

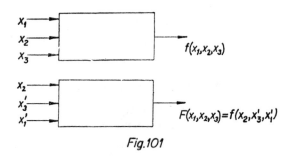

Fig.101

mapping θ can be realized simply by applying the variables (possibly negated) to the inputs in a different order. This transforms the function $f(x_1, x_2, x_3)$ into a new function, namely,

$$F(x_1, x_2, x_3) = f(x_2, x'_3, x'_1).$$

If, for example,

$$\begin{aligned}
f(x_1, x_2, x_3) &= x_1 x'_2 x_3 + x_1 x'_2 x_3 + x'_1 x'_2 x_3 + x'_1 x_2 x_3 \\
&= x_1 x'_2 + x'_1 x_3,
\end{aligned}$$

we have,

$$\begin{aligned}
F(x_1, x_2, x_3) &= \Delta f(x_1, x_2, x_3) \\
&= x_2 x_3 x_1 + x_2 x_3 x'_1 + x'_2 x_3 x'_1 + x'_2 x'_3 x'_1 \\
&= x_2 x_3 + x'_2 x'_1.
\end{aligned}$$

An equivalence class consists of those functions which result from a certain circuit, if the variables are applied to the inputs in a different order and selectively negated.

The number of equivalence classes in the set F_3 is equal to the number of non-congruent vertex configurations on the cube. We find that if 0, 1, 7 or 8 vertices are marked then there is always one class; for 2, 3, 4 and 6 vertices, 3 classes; and for 4 vertices, 6 classes; i.e. 22 classes altogether. Figure 102 shows the three configurations for 3 marked vertices.

Fig.102

The corresponding classification of the switching functions in two variables can be easily carried out by the reader. It is based on the symmetry transformations of the square; this is a group of order 8. In a similar manner, a classification of the set F_n may be achieved for higher n. In this case we have to consider the group of symmetry transformations of the n-dimensional cube. This group has the order $2^n n$!

BIBLIOGRAPHY

The bibliography of the German edition listed 20 books of which the following are available in English.

[1] The A.T.M. Handbook; *Some Lessons in Mathematics*, Cambridge University Press, London, 1965

[2] GNEDENKO, B. V. and KHINCHIN, A. YA; *An Elementary Introduction to the Theory of Probability*, Freeman, San Francisco, 1961.

[3] GOLDBERG, S.; *Probability*, Prentice Hall, Englewood Cliffs, (N.J.), 1960

[4] KEMENY, J. G. *et al.*; *Introduction to Finite Mathematics*, Prentice Hall, Englewood Cliffs (N.J.), 1957

[5] KEMENY, J. G. *et al;. Finite Mathematical Structures*, Prentice Hall, Englewood Cliffs (N.J.), 1959

[6] LIPSCHUTZ, E.; *Set Theory and Related Topics*, Schaum, New York, 1964

[7] RIORDAN, J.; *An Introduction to Combinatorial Analysis*, Wiley, New York, 1958

[8] RYSER, H. J.; *Combinatorial Analysis*, Wiley, New York, 1963

[9] SHANNON, C. E.; 'A Symbolic Analysis of Relay and Switching Circuits', *Trans. A.I.E.E.*, Vol 57, 1938

[10] WHITESITT, J. E.; *Boolean Algebra and its Applications*, Addison Wesley, Reading (Mass.), 1960

[11] YAGLOM, A. M. and YAGLOM, Y. M.; *Challenging Mathematical Problems with Elementary Solutions*, Vol 1, Holden-Day, San Francisco, 1964

These books cater for a wide variety of interests and are by no means written with the same range of readers in mind. For example, [1] contains an account of how some of the ideas of set-theory and Boolean algebra can be introduced into the lower forms of the secondary school; whereas the aim of [8], which is one of the Carus Mathematical Monographs published by the Mathematical Association of America, is to 'pursue certain topics with thoroughness and reach the frontiers of present-day research'. Books such as [5] and [10], however, would prove reasonable sequels to this volume.

Further books in English dealing with Boolean algebra and lattice theory are listed below. [12], which contains a proof of Stone's Theorem and work on sentence logic, is written at around the same level as the present book. Chapter XIV of [13] considers lattices in the framework of the recent functional approach to algebra—this book will doubtless become one of the classics of mathematics but it is not easy reading. [14] is the latest edition of one of the key books on lattice theory first published in 1940.

The advanced student wishing to read further about measure theory and the theory of probability will find a challenging account in [15].

[12] GOODSTEIN, R. L.; *Boolean Algebra*, Pergamon Press, Oxford, 1963

[13] MacLANE, S. and BIRKHOFF, G.; *Algebra*, Macmillan, New York, 1967

[14] BIRKHOFF, G.; *Lattice Theory* (3rd Edn.), American Mathematical Society, Providence (N.J.), 1966

[15] KINGMAN, J. F. C. and TAYLOR, S. J.; *Introduction to Measure and Probability*, Cambridge University Press, London, 1966

INDEX